THE
LANDMARK
HANDBOOK
FOURTEENTH EDITION
1994

EDITED BY CHARLOTTE HASLAM
PUBLISHED BY THE LANDMARK TRUST
SHOTTESBROOKE, MAIDENHEAD, BERKSHIRE SL6 3SW
(TELEPHONE: 0628 825925)

Knowle Hill in 1795, by Robert Marris

Derby Museum

Contents

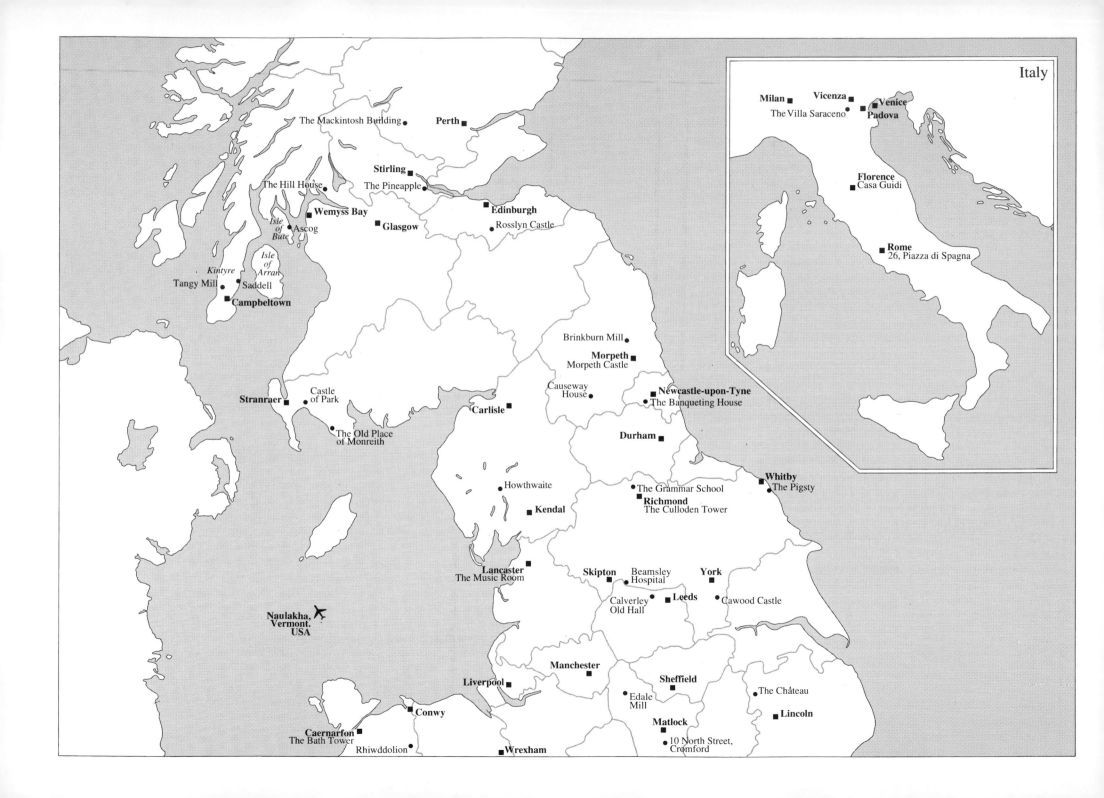

Italy

Milan
Vicenza
The Villa Saraceno
Venice
Padova

Florence
Casa Guidi

Rome
26, Piazza di Spagna

The Mackintosh Building
Perth

Stirling
The Hill House
The Pineapple

Wemyss Bay
Ascog
Isle of Bute
Edinburgh
Rosslyn Castle
Glasgow

Isle of Arran
Kintyre
Tangy Mill
Saddell
Campbeltown

Brinkburn Mill
Morpeth
Morpeth Castle
Causeway House
Stranraer
Castle of Park
Newcastle-upon-Tyne
The Banqueting House
Carlisle
The Old Place of Monreith
Durham

Whitby
The Pigsty
Howthwaite
The Grammar School
Richmond
The Culloden Tower
Kendal

Lancaster
The Music Room
Skipton
Beamsley Hospital
York
Calverley Old Hall
Leeds
Cawood Castle

Naulakha, Vermont. USA

Manchester
Liverpool
Sheffield
Edale Mill
The Château
Conwy
Lincoln
Caernarfon
The Bath Tower
Matlock
Rhiwddolion
Wrexham
10 North Street, Cromford

Plas Uchaf
Alton Station
Nottingham
Grantham
St. Winifred's Well
Ingestre Pavilion
Derby
Appleton Water Tower
Swarkestone Pavilion
The House of Correction
King's Lynn
Poultry Cottage
Shrewsbury
Stafford
Tixall Gatehouse
Knowle Hill
Norwich
34 High Street, Ironbridge
Langley Gatehouse
Leicester
Peterborough
Montgomery
The White House
Birmingham
Lynch Lodge
Manor Farm
Bromfield Priory Gatehouse
Ludlow
Lock Cottage
The New Inn
Cardigan
Worcester
Stratford-upon-Avon
The Bath House
Northampton
Cambridge
Bury St. Edmunds
Church Cottage
Stockwell Farm
Shelwick Court
The Tower, Canons Ashby
Bedford
Ipswich
Aldeburgh
The Martello Tower
Maesyronen Chapel
Hereford
East Banqueting House
The Gothic Temple
Warden Abbey
Purton Green
St. David's
15 Tower Hill
Carmarthen
Tower Hill Lodge
Brecon
Tewkesbury
St Mary's Lane
The Abbey Gatehouse
Buckingham
Abergavenny
Gloucester
Oxford
7, St. Michael's Street
The West Blockhouse
Clytha Castle
Cirencester
Field House
The Old Parsonage
City of London
Cloth Fair
Pembroke
Monkton Old Hall
Bristol
Hampton Court Palace
Bath
Marshal Wade's House
Maidstone
The Prospect Tower
Woodspring Priory
Stogursey Castle
Wells
The Old Hall
Hole Cottage
Dover
Lundy
Gurney Manor
Church House
Salisbury
The Wardrobe
Bideford
The Library
Taunton
Laughton Place
Peppercombe
Southampton
Lewes
Coombe
The Priest's House
Fox Hall
Chichester
The College
Shute Gatehouse
Margells
Woodsford Castle
Luttrell's Tower
Exeter
Launceston
Wortham Manor
Lettaford
Peters Tower
Dorchester
Endsleigh
Whiteford Temple
The Danescombe Mine
Plymouth
Kingswear Castle
Lower Porthmeor
Truro
Penzance
The Egyptian House
Frenchman's Creek
Alderney
Fort Clonque
Channel Islands
Guernsey
Jersey
The Nicolle Tower

Introduction

The Landmark Trust is a charity which rescues buildings in distress and brings them back to useful life. It was founded some thirty years ago to tackle cases too desperate, troublesome or unfashionable for anyone else. These usually involve minor but good-looking buildings, put up with thought and care, but no longer wanted for their original purpose, and heading for destruction or decay unless a new use can be found for them.

Often the best solution, so it seems to us, is to let them for holidays. There is seldom a suitable public use. To turn them into permanent homes may be impossible, or call for alterations and additions which would spoil them. As the weekend or holiday retreats of individual owners they would lie empty and unenjoyed for most of the year; but let by us they are occupied almost all the time, and an income is generated for their maintenance.

Moreover, in this way a constant succession of different people can actually live, however briefly, in historic buildings of every age and style. By sleeping under its roof they profit far more from each place than by paying to look at it only; they can study it at leisure, be there early and late, and get the feel of its surroundings. We believe that by using our buildings thus, where possible combined with ordinary public access, the maximum number of people derive the most benefit from them; and that many visitors who may come just for a holiday go home with a new interest awakened which will last them all their lives.

So far we have worked, or are working, on over 200 buildings, in all parts of these islands, and abroad on four which have important links with this country. Many have come our way through schemes undertaken with the National Trust or other charities, or with local authorities. A few (not shown in this Handbook) we have, after restoring them, sold or given away to other charities, but the remainder we have kept. All are remarkable in some way—for their architecture, history, atmosphere or situation. We have no favourite period or style, although we lean towards the humble and the functional.

Inevitably some are cottages or houses, but we try not to take out of the 'housing stock' any building which stands a good chance of being made into a satisfactory modern home without spoiling it—and in fact we have some fifty long-term tenants. A little to our surprise, letting a building for short periods, especially outside so-called holiday areas, often rather pleases the neighbours (where there are any) by producing for them a succession of interested newcomers—and customers—some of whom find themselves caught up in the life of the place, particularly in winter.

Most of the buildings we tackle need a great deal doing to them. We aim at work of the highest quality—and in this way try to preserve skill as well as buildings—but we do not like our places in what Queen Victoria called 'a very high state of preservation'. It is not easy to combine good and lasting work with a restrained approach; and there is always a temptation, and sometimes pressure, to make everything as good as new while we are at it. This is most marked with derelict timber-framed buildings. To repair these ruins of wood and plaster, eaten by English weather, is like patching a cobweb. The urge is often powerful to replace too much, but the result is a building which has lost all feeling, and which looks as miserable as a small boy cleaned up by a tough mother.

We do not go in for 'conjectural' restoration. If some element of a building is missing altogether we only provide a modern replacement when it is quite certain what it was like originally, and if the building would look ridiculous without it. On the other hand we do believe that sometimes later additions may be removed and later changes reversed. Alterations made to a building are part of its history and so there should be a presumption in favour of keeping them—unless the original design is of much higher quality than later and perhaps dilapidated work which mars it. In addition we do not wish (and cannot afford) to preserve our buildings as dead objects. They are to be occupied by human beings who cook and wash and use the rooms. Occasionally therefore we need to make with care some fresh alteration to a building—and we hope that in so doing we add further to its history. These are the principles to which we keep, when we are not bullied out of them by the authorities.

In the course of our work with buildings we have also carried out many schemes, now invisible, for the removal of wire-scapes, eyesores and clutter. Adding things, even well-meant things like seats, notices and items of 'street furniture', seldom improves a place, whereas taking things away nearly always does.

When fitting out our places for occupation we do not make them luxurious or smart (although some are quite grand); they are just made as practical and comfortable as their nature allows. All have heating of one kind or another so that they can be used all the year round, which we are very keen that they should be. We also take much trouble when furnishing them, aiming to please the eye and interest people without being at all extravagant; almost all our furniture is old and good, unpretentious and carefully chosen—indeed we find ourselves rescuing furniture in distress as well as buildings, by buying (and repairing) just those plain admirable pieces with which England used to abound. Most of the curtains are specially designed and printed, by us, for each place. The rugs and carpets are exceptional, if seldom in their first youth. All the pictures, however humble, have some special reason for being there. We are trying to preserve and restore not only the buildings but also the outlook on life which created them.

We also provide each Landmark with those books which we think that an enquiring visitor would like to find there—books about the neighbourhood and works of literature with local associations—and an album of historical notes, plans and photographs, showing how the place was when we found it and what we have done to it. There are also large scale maps of the neighbourhood marking the footpaths. A stay in a Landmark is meant to offer not just a holiday but an experience, of a mildly elevating kind, a fresh window on life, to be looked through, or not, as you please.

Achieving all this, and maintaining it in buildings constantly occupied and used, is not easy, and grateful thanks are due to our staff, many of whom put so much into their work that it becomes an art of its own.

Who stays in our places? Alas, we seldom meet them, but we know a good deal about them because each Landmark has a logbook in which visitors can write whatever they like for the benefit of their successors. Here, released from the strait-jacket of daily life, they reveal great enterprise and imagination. They find and record the most fascinating things to see and do, of greater variety than ever we could have suggested to them. Most people during their stay make for themselves some discovery or other. A few disappoint us by using their cars too much, but others are content just to be there, giving their cars a rest as well as themselves; and a noble few come by public transport, which serves many of our places very adequately. At Landmarks in towns our visitors seem to like having their own front door instead of staying in a hotel; as David Copperfield said 'it was a wonderfully fine thing to walk about town with the key of my house in my pocket'. More and more come from abroad. A surprising number are not on holiday at all, but come to do or to study something in particular. Very many return, to the same Landmark, or to others in succession; and it warms the heart when they write 'I dream of staying again in each and every one'. Some sound so charming, that one longs to meet them. Though every party occupies a Landmark for a very short time, the logbook links them with those who come before and after, and gives to them and to the place a sense of continuity. These logbooks reward us for our labours, and show what real pleasure people, given half a chance, can still find in our battered island.

Many of the buildings we take on have a special reason for being in trouble. To rescue these may need perseverance just as much as money. Sometimes a building has been stranded without access; more often it is owned or controlled by someone who thinks that it would be a nuisance to him if it were restored and used. But in fact our sort of use, because it is unassertive, and does not require outworks such as garages or elaborate gardens—or indeed, if needs must, any land at all outside the actual building—is usually far less of a nuisance and worry to an owner than is any other solution whatever. We try to persuade people of this, but it is hard work, taking sometimes many years; and we have had unfortunate failures, when we have been in the end prevented from saving a building which, once saved, would have given pleasure and edification for generations. It is also dreadful to think of all the buildings of our kind which were thoughtlessly destroyed before we were in a position to do anything about them; but time has closed over them and that is that.

Those who care about our surroundings fight under a handicap. When a fine building is demolished, or a fine place spoilt, that is the end of the matter; but the destroyer, if driven off, can always try again. To win at all we have to win every time, whereas the forces of destruction need win but once. We are inevitably on the defensive, appearing indeed to fight a rearguard action only; and it is all too easy for those who destroy to represent those who care as backward-looking and obstructive. But the reverse is the truth. Material progress has at least meant that we no longer have to foul our surroundings in order to survive. Indeed it now seems that we cannot survive if we do. It is those who still preach cheapness at any price who are out of date; while those who preach against waste, whether of buildings or of other resources, are modern. Far from being restrictive, preservation is now constructive, and creative as well, and those who care about the environment are in fact in the vanguard of progress and part of a growing army.

Moreover the Landmark Trust is not just engaged in preservation. It is trying to make 'preservation' unnecessary by opening the eyes of as many people as possible to what is being done to this planet and its occupants. Indeed our aim is to rouse people's interest in their surroundings in the widest sense—their surroundings both in space and time. The environment is not just a film set, as so many in the 'Heritage industry' now regard it. History is part of our environment; so is the way people live, their scale of values, and how they treat each other and the rest of creation. We shall not, of course, attain this grandiose objective, but if we can just nudge cannonball of progress in its flight, then we shall be content. We hope that every day some of our many guests, as they set up house in one or other of our many places, will feel that 'here a man may . . . be thinking what he is, whence he came, what he has done, and to what the King has called him'.

John Smith

vii

Staying in a Landmark

All the properties described in the main section of this Handbook can be rented by anyone, for periods ranging from a weekend up to a maximum of three weeks. You do not have to be a member to book—a copy of the Handbook, and a price list, are all you need.

Most people take our buildings for holidays. Others use them to write or compose, as a base for study in the area, or as somewhere for a working team to think and talk. They are available all the year round, in winter as well as summer. Every building has been chosen by us not only because it needed our help, but also because we believe people will enjoy staying in it.

Many were in desperate condition when we took them on. Much painstaking and costly work has gone into making them as they are now. We believe strongly in the importance of good detail, inside and out, from the quality of pointing to the design of a window latch; from hand-printed curtains to cutlery. As far as possible, we preserve our buildings in the form in which they were built. The living arrangements as a result can be interesting and unusual.

Within this framework, we aim for a high standard of comfort—the more you feel at home, the more you and the building will benefit each other. All buildings have modern bathrooms and kitchens, and kitchen equipment—large ones have dishwashers too. While in most respects, every Landmark is different, in this, all are the same. Old Chelsea crockery will greet you in Scotland, Cornwall or Kent. All beds, however ancient

and exotic the head and foot, have new sprung-mattresses, blankets and pillows. We also provide linen and towels (but not for cots).

All buildings have heating, mainly by night storage, and the majority have an open fire or stove as well. We do not provide logs or coal, but neither do we charge extra for gas or electricity.

In a Landmark, we hope to take you away from modern distractions, so none of our buildings has a television, and only where there is some compelling reason is there a telephone. Instead, they have books, maps and jigsaws; writing desks, armchairs and log fires—and secret corners for hide-and-seek.

It is even possible to leave your car behind: it is not just properties in towns that are well served by public transport. If you do come by car, in one or two cases you must park it some distance from the house, so you can forget about it for a few days without much difficulty.

In nearly all cases, we own enough land with our buildings to give you somewhere to sit outside—a few have exceptional gardens. This is not always possible in towns or villages, but even then there might be a terrace or flat roof. Sometimes, we own the surrounding fields. These are usually let for grazing, but you are free to walk or play there. Really well-behaved dogs are welcome at most properties, unless the problems or temptations are too great for them.

Most important of all, every Landmark has a House-keeper, who will prepare it for your arrival. Some of them knew the building long before we did, or have cared for it as long as we have. They can be invisible, if you wish, but many become friends, and talking to them and getting to know them is part of the pleasure of the holiday.

We prefer to let our buildings by the week, but they can be booked for shorter stays, weekends or mid-week, from early November until late March. Bookings for whole weeks can be made at any time for any period in the current and two next calendar years. For shorter stays, please refer to the price list, which gives details of this and much else that you will need to know.

All bookings are best made over the telephone (**0628 825925, Monday to Friday: 9.00 a.m.–7.00 p.m.; Saturday and Sunday: 10.00 a.m.–4.00 p.m.**), since we can then answer questions immediately, and can suggest alternatives if your first choice is not available.

We aim in this Handbook to give you as much information as possible to help you make that choice. Each building is illustrated and described, giving something of its story and the reasons for which we (and sometimes others) think it is special. There are maps suggesting places nearby that we think worth visiting. The plans show you how the accommodation in each is arranged, particularly with regard to beds.

Changes do take place during the year, however, especially in those buildings where work is still in progress at the time the Handbook is printed. Here again it is important to check the price list.

Even then, there may still be more that you want to know about spending a holiday in a Landmark. If so, please ring our Booking Office. They already have, or can quickly find out, the answers to a multitude of questions.

Edale Mill, Derbyshire

The Culloden Tower, Richmond, Yorkshire

Laughton Place, Sussex

Ingestre Pavilion, Staffordshire

Margells, Branscombe, Devon

Cawood Castle, Yorkshire

The Pigsty, Robin Hood's Bay, Yorkshire

The Bath House, Walton, Warwickshire

Fox Hall, Charlton, Sussex

The Old Hall, Croscombe, Somerset

Brinkburn Mill, Northumberland

Helping the Landmark Trust

I hope you will agree when you have looked through this Handbook that direct action by the Landmark Trust has resulted in many of the country's finest small buildings being preserved for our own and future generations to enjoy. Every one of them has something valuable to give us–a wider understanding of history, a fresh look at our surroundings, or a new knowledge of traditional building skills.

A gift or bequest to the Landmark Trust will help to ensure that this important work is continued; and could be directly responsible for saving a building which might otherwise be lost.

Everyone who rents a Landmark for their holiday is contributing to its upkeep. A proportion of that rental income also goes towards new work, but it can only be a small one: the cost of maintaining a high standard of furnishing and care in our 150 existing, constantly used, buildings is inevitably great.

Money to pay for each new project has therefore to come from elsewhere. As a registered charity, the Landmark Trust receives no guaranteed grant from the Government or other charitable sources. Obviously we seek such help whenever possible, but for this we are just one among many applicants. Our funding for new work is therefore not secure and legacies, in particular, help us enormously to plan for the future.

The pressures for Landmark intervention are as great as ever. We receive details of several buildings at risk every week, but we do not have the funds to take on more than a small percentage of them. A gift by way of a legacy, however modest, would be a direct and positive contribution to the Trust's work and would enable others to benefit, as perhaps you have done, from living for a short time in an historic building.

If you would like more information on making a bequest, please do contact me.

Robin Evans
Director

The Swiss Cottage, at Endsleigh in Devon, in 1977

Landmark Supporters

If you would like to know more about our work and at the same time meet other people who stay in Landmarks, you can now enroll as a Supporter. The annual fee of £35 entitles you to buy tickets for yourself and a guest to any of the special open days and events organised throughout the year. You will also receive a free copy of each new edition of the Handbook as soon as it is published. Application forms are available from Shottesbrooke.

The Swiss Cottage as it is today

The Swarkestone Pavilion, Derbyshire, in 1986

The Swarkestone Pavilion as it is today

On the stairs at Warden Abbey

The Landmark Trust

Alton Station, Staffordshire

This is the only Italianate railway station in Staffordshire, a notable example of a vanishing class of building. We were indeed grateful to the County Council for conveying it to us in 1970. The railway has gone; but in its heyday the platforms took 12-coach excursion trains from the Potteries.

Its architect was probably H. A. Hunt, an architect-engineer who designed other stations on this line, opened in 1849. Built by the North Staffordshire Railway (the 'Knotty') to a befitting standard for the Earl of Shrewsbury, then owner of Alton Towers, it stands in marvellous surroundings, both beautiful and interesting. Pugin's Alton Castle rises out of the trees across the valley of the Churnet, like something from the Carinthia of Dornford Yates; and Alton Towers itself, with its famous garden, lies immediately behind.

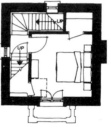

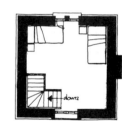

During our work on the house a disused flue was found to have been blocked with porters' waistcoats; and the plumbing we installed produced at first a strange chuffing sound—doubtless the yearning of this house for the sound and smell of great engines wreathed in steam. Our housekeeper, Mrs Bowers, was one of the last passengers to travel on the line. She still has her ticket from Leek to Alton (fare 3/–) dated 2 Jan 1965.

FIRST FLOOR

SECOND FLOOR

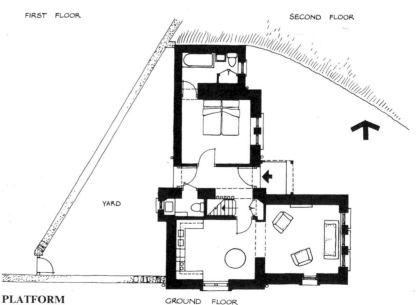

PLATFORM

YARD

GROUND FLOOR

Appleton Water Tower, Nr. King's Lynn, Norfolk

A public-spirited local landowner gave us a lease of this exceptional Victorian tower. There is seldom an opportunity to preserve a functional building such as this, let alone one of such quality. It was designed by Robert Rawlinson and the foundation stone was laid in July 1877 by the Princess of Wales. On the ground and first floor was a dwelling for the custodian with a viewing room above reached by an outside stair. The flues from all the fireplaces passed through the centre of the iron tank to prevent the water from freezing—a typically Victorian idea, original, simple and practical.

From the terrace on top of the tank, which is protected by an ornate cast iron railing, and from the room below, there is a view on all sides over miles of this wide, open, landscape, with a distant gleam of the Wash.

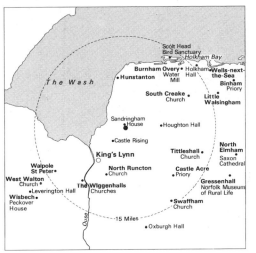

From the logbook

"A toad guards the steps by the side gate and the garden is alive with wild animals and birds: we saw a deer on the lawn one evening".

"Much time was spent on top viewing the countryside through binoculars, watching the sun set and looking at the stars on clear nights".

"Time a walk from Stiffkey to ensure you miss the incoming tide and you can go 3 miles towards Blakeney Point. We got within 50 yards of the seals without scaring them off".

"Squeals of excitement as we explored the Tower".

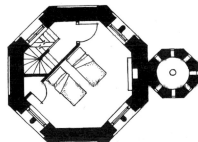
FIRST FLOOR

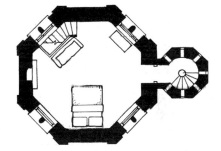
SECOND FLOOR

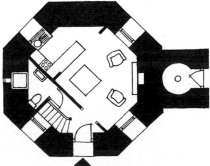
GROUND FLOOR

Ascog, Isle of Bute, Strathclyde

Bute has been called the Scottish Isle of Wight, and certainly Rothesay, its capital, with its Winter Garden and decorative ironwork, is reminiscent of the South Coast. It is also very easy to get to, by ferry from Wemyss Bay, less than an hour from Glasgow.

Ascog lies on the sheltered east coast of the island. Trees (especially beech) and shrubs (Mackintosh drew fuschias here) grow lushly in its mild climate. It was gently developed as a superior resort from the 1840s on, with a scattering of respectable houses above the bay—building on the shoreline was wisely forbidden.

One such house stands in the large and secluded grounds of the old mansion house of Ascog, once home to a branch of the Stewarts. We have acquired both buildings, which stand a few hundred yards apart, each looking over its own, rather different, garden.

Ascog House is a typical laird's house of the seventeenth century. We have removed some clumsy Victorian additions, to restore its true proportions and dignified character. The main rooms are on the first floor, reached by a wide turnpike stair. They have old fireplaces and windows in deep embrasures, overlooking the rediscovered paths and terraces of a late Victorian formal garden, said to have been designed by Edward Latrobe-Bateman.

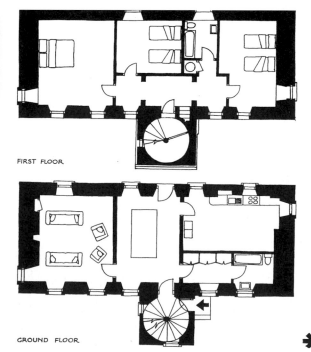

FIRST FLOOR

GROUND FLOOR

TURRET ROOM

There is another twin bedroom and bathroom in Tom's Tower, 20 feet from the main house

4

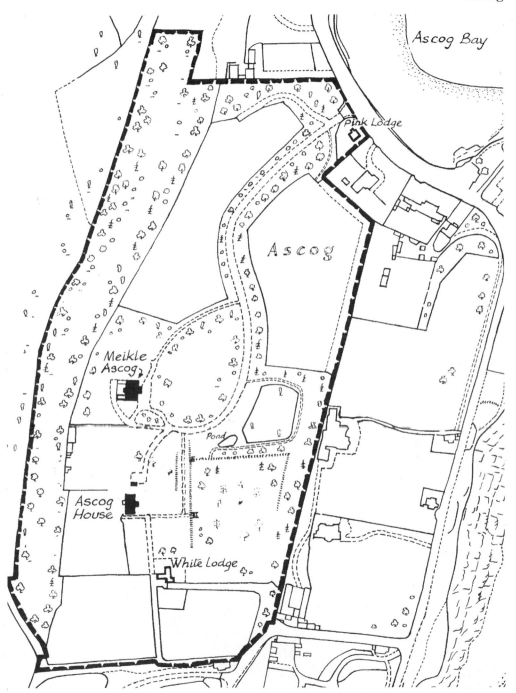

Ascog

Meikle Ascog is what nineteenth century guide books called a neat villa. Its builder, and possibly designer, was an engineer called Robert Thom, who bought the property in 1830. Thom's greatest achievement (besides the sensitive development of Ascog) was to succeed where engineers such as Watt and Rennie had failed, in the quest to provide Greenock with water—the loch from which it comes is named after him.

In its arrangement, his house reflects a logical and inventive personality, being laid out in the most rational way possible to achieve the most agreeable result: every room is pleasant to be in. The windows look out over a shrubbery, with the sea and the mainland beyond, framed by fine trees. Low sills in the drawing room and dining room ensure that this view can be enjoyed, even when sitting down.

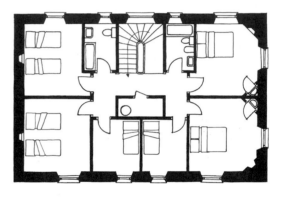

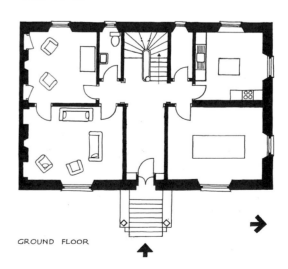

FIRST FLOOR

GROUND FLOOR

The Banqueting House, Gibside, Nr. Newcastle

Gibside was inherited in 1722 by George Bowes, a landowner and public figure made rich by coal. After his first wife died, he made Gibside his home and set about embellishing the park. The Banqueting House seems to have been finished by 1746. It was designed by Daniel Garrett, a former assistant of Lord Burlington's, to stand in the highest part of the park, looking over the Derwent valley.

When we first saw the Banqueting House in 1977 it was almost entirely roofless, and the porch and crocketed gables had collapsed. The park, now happily transferred to the National Trust by the Earl of Strathmore, was then let to the Forestry Commission and the Banqueting House was hidden by trees.

Here was, however, an important building of most original design, part of a famous landscape. The Forestry Commission agreed to give up their lease of it and the Strathmore Estate then sold us the freehold. Most of the missing stonework was found nearby and inside we were able to save much of the plaster-work and joinery of one room. But the Great Room was just a shell: here we replaced only the main elements of Garrett's design, known from an old photograph.

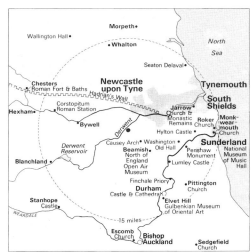

The Banqueting House now stands in a grassy clearing, looking down to an octagonal pool and the valley beyond. A few hundred yards away the Column of British Liberty rises high above the trees, and a little further off lies the Gibside chapel, designed by James Paine in 1760 to hold the remains of George Bowes, ancestor of our Queen.

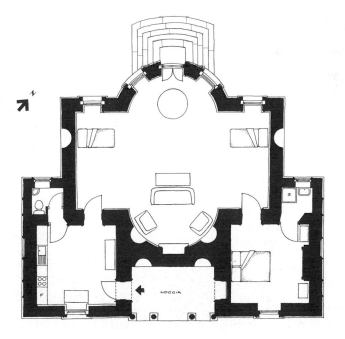

The Bath House, Walton, Stratford-upon-Avon, Warwickshire

The benefits of a cold bath were held to be almost limitless by medical opinion of the eighteenth century, and few gentlemen failed to equip themselves with one. The Bath House here, it is thought, was designed in 1748 by the gentleman-architect Sanderson Miller for his friend Sir Charles Mordaunt. Good historical fun was had by all: the rough masonry of Antiquity, used for the bath chamber, is contrasted with the polished smoothness of the new Augustan age, seen in the room above, where the bathers recovered.

Even in the upper room there is a hint of the subterranean, with a dome hung with coolly dripping icicles. To take the imagery of the grotto one stage further, shells decorate the walls, but shells that are happy in the drawing room, arranged in festoons as if 'by some invisible sea-nymph or triton for their private amusement'. This was the idea of Mrs Delany, better known for her flower pictures, who arranged the shells herself with the help of Mordaunt daughters. Their work has been skilfully reproduced for us by Diana Reynell, after terrible damage by vandals.

The Bath House, leased to us by its owner, has one room to live in, but in its deep woodland setting, so near to the Forest of Arden, 'you may fleet the time carelessly, as they did in the golden world'.

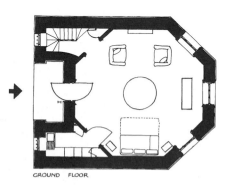

GROUND FLOOR

The bathroom is upstairs, above the porch

The Bath Tower, Caernarfon

This is one of the towers of the medieval town wall, facing the Menai Strait. More recently, it was part of a Public Bath House, built in 1823 to attract tourists to the town. The present living room was perhaps a Reading Room. Its two great windows look along the outside to the town wall in one direction, and across the Strait in the other. Here you can have your cake and eat it—the sea at your feet in front; and the pleasures of an interesting town at your back.

The tower had been empty for some long time when we bought it. Both entrances are very striking—one along a narrow alley from the street behind, the other from the sea wall. Below the living room, reached by a spiral stair, there is a very large room in which you can sleep like soldiers of the Edwardian garrison. But if there are only two of you, you can sleep in seclusion at the top of the tower, with just the sky and the battlements.

From the logbook

"We put the children in the dungeon which they thoroughly enjoyed".

"A medieval atmosphere has been achieved without the discomforts of the period".

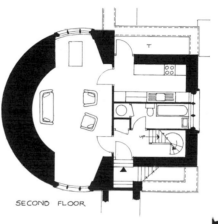

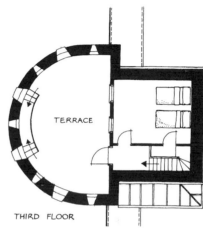

"To have lived in a building, if only for one short week, whose traditions reach so far back in history has been a worthwhile experience".

"I like the curtains very much".

"The library was a complete surprise and was particularly enjoyed when we were alone".

SECOND FLOOR

THIRD FLOOR

TERRACE

FIRST FLOOR

STEPS TO CELLAR AND DOOR TO QUAY

Beamsley Hospital, Nr. Skipton, Yorkshire

Almshouses are a familiar ingredient in our towns and villages, but the Hospital at Beamsley is more unusual. Behind the conventional row of dwellings on the road lies this circular stone building. In it were rooms for seven women, encircling a chapel, through which most of them had to pass to reach their doors, a daily encouragement to piety. Until the 1970s the little community of Mother and Sisters lived here, their lives governed by ancient, and ferociously strict, rules.

The Hospital was founded in 1593 by the Countess of Cumberland, at a time when the poor had only private charity to depend on. Her building is an Elizabethan conceit, alluding, perhaps, both to her husband's coat of arms and to the round churches of the Templars. Her daughter, that formidable northern heroine Lady Anne Clifford, added the front range. She also furnished the chapel and, almshouses being of their nature conservative places, these fittings survive.

Finding the buildings no longer in demand, the Trustees offered them to us. The front range we have let to long-term tenants; and you will

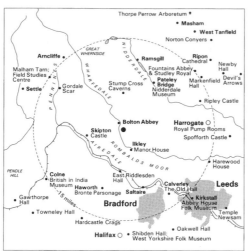

stay in the other. Using its oddly-shaped rooms, and repeatedly crossing the chapel (whose bell still rings), is a curious experience, bringing you close to the subtle yet vigorous Elizabethan mind. And all around is Yorkshire at its highest and most unadulterated.

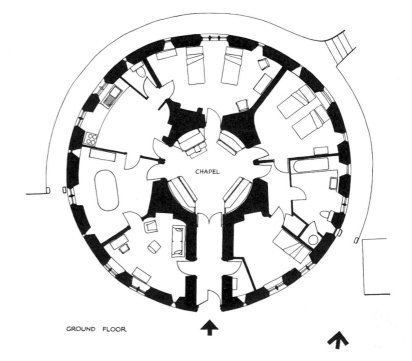

CHAPEL

GROUND FLOOR

10

Brinkburn Mill, Rothbury, Northumberland

When a priory was founded here about 1135, the monks, with typical skill, identified one place in this otherwise steep and thickly-wooded ravine where there was enough level ground for their buildings. These stood in a loop of the River Coquet, which provided, among other things, water to drive a mill.

The present mill lies at the end of a long lawn, looking back towards the pretty Gothick manor house that stands beside the soaring priory church. This mill was built, about 1800, near the site of its medieval predecessor, but was later dressed up to improve the view from the house. The wheel and grinding stones are still here, although long unused.

At the upper end of the mill, and previously separate from it, are two grander rooms. These may have been an office or perhaps a fishing lodge. One is now the sitting room, with tall windows facing west to catch the evening sun.

Of Brinkburn's setting one historian wrote: 'This is the most deep solitude, chosen for a religious edifice, I ever yet visited'. The same can be said of the mill, reached by its own drive through the woods (once the main approach to the priory) with only the sound of the river for company. A walk among the priory buildings in the early morning is recommended.

From the logbook

"Peaceful. Very peaceful in fact. Brilliant walks".

"Castles, moors, houses and gardens—all are worth visiting, none have been disappointing".

"Down by the Coquet is a good place for skimming stones. I got a niner this morning".

"Lucky to have almost unbroken sunshine—there were gales in the world outside. Craster kippers are justly renowned".

"We enjoyed being able to stroll over to the Priory and then come back for a cup of tea".

"We said we'd come back, and we have".

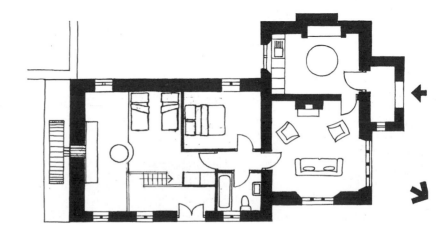

Bromfield Priory Gatehouse, Ludlow, Shropshire

The Benedictine monks of Bromfield Priory added a new stone gatehouse to their precinct before 1400. After the Dissolution a timber-framed upper storey was added to this. The room over the arch was used for the manorial court, and later, from 1836 until 1895, for the village school. A teacher's cottage was added at one end, and the Gatehouse was generally done up in a Picturesque manner.

Afterwards it became for many years the parish reading and recreation room, complete with billiard table, and came in useful for meetings of various sorts, from the youth club to the teaching of first aid. This functional character has rubbed off on the schoolroom itself, which is large and plain and a little bit musty. At one end, a chimneypiece and large cupboards have been put together from an odd assortment of Jacobean carving.

The gatehouse now opens onto a grassy churchyard. In front runs a private road, leading only to a few farms and to Oakly Park (lodge by C. R. Cockerell), successor to the Tudor priory house whose ruins can still be seen on the south side of the parish church. Bromfield itself is an estate village, and South Shropshire, with Ludlow as its capital, is deep country still.

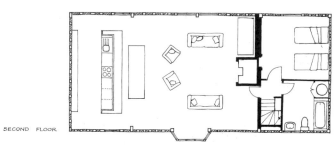

SECOND FLOOR

FIRST FLOOR

GROUND FLOOR

Calverley Old Hall, Nr. Leeds, West Yorkshire

When we arrived on the scene, this ancient house, seat of the Calverley family for over five hundred years, had long been divided into cottages and was about to be sold in slices. To save it from this fate, we bought the whole of it, and the open ground in front.

The Calverleys were minor Yorkshire magnates, often knighted and latterly baronets. One, put to death after murdering his two eldest sons here—not in the part of the house you will stay in—was the subject of a play, *The Yorkshire Tragedy*, once claimed to be by Shakespeare. Another, it is said, was the model for Sir Roger de Coverley. After the Civil War, when they had to pay a crippling fine to keep their property, the Calverley of the day married the heiress of Esholt Hall, nearby, and from then on the family spent most of their time there.

So Calverley Old Hall went slowly down in the world, and in 1754 was sold to the Thornhills, whose descendants sold it to us. Blackened and stoney in the romantic Northern manner, but still quite grand, it is now surrounded by lesser houses. We have so far repaired the chapel, the hammer-beam hall roof and one wing, the **North House**, in which you will stay.

This is not a place to judge on first impressions. But the close-knit, friendly life of the neighbouring streets, of corner shop and pub, soon warms all those who come here. There are many good things in the area to visit by day, before returning in the evening to ponder, under the moulded beams, on the vanished Calverleys and their once-great house.

The South front with the chapel and the great hall to the right of it. The North House is at the far end of the wing running back on the left

Inside the North House

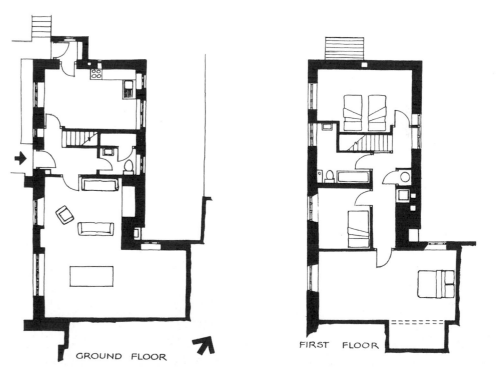

GROUND FLOOR

FIRST FLOOR

Castle of Park, Glenluce, Galloway

Thomas Hay of Park, son of the last abbot of Glenluce, is said to have used stone from the Abbey for his new tower house, begun in 1590. In the 1970s, after standing empty for over a century, the tower was repaired by Historic Scotland, present guardians of the Abbey. In 1990, they leased the tower to us, and we have completed their work and made it habitable.

Standing on a tree-fringed plateau above Luce Bay, the building, as often with tower houses, is outwardly plain. Inside, it is a different matter, especially now that the walls are plastered again, and the rooms furnished. This gives a very different impression of the life of a Jacobean laird to that gained from the stony shells of so many abandoned towers.

The hall is thirty feet long, with a fine fireplace. From it the laird's private stair leads to bedrooms, each with its own privy (the potential for hide and seek is endless). The wide main stair, in its own tower, has a little room at the top called the cap-house, from which you can glimpse the sea.

The eighteenth century brought larger

windows, to let in more light—the bright, clear, light of a western peninsular. There are notable gardens to visit nearby, and the rolling fields are grazed by cattle, seemingly more numerous than the human inhabitants.

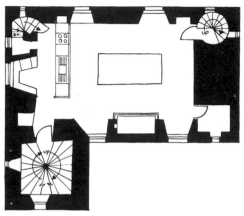

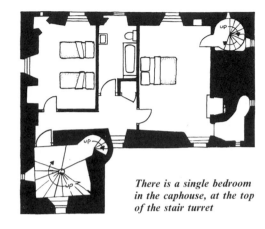

There is a single bedroom in the caphouse, at the top of the stair turret

FIRST FLOOR

THIRD FLOOR

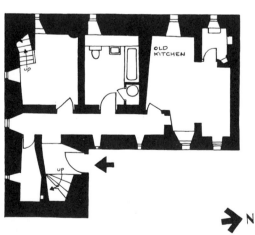

GROUND FLOOR

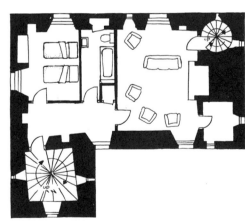

SECOND FLOOR

14

15

Casa Guidi, Piazza S. Felice, Florence, Italy

Pen Browning, son of the poets Elizabeth and Robert, wished his parents' Florentine home, in which they had spent nearly all the happy and productive years of their marriage, to be recreated in their memory. He did not live to see his wish fulfilled, but it was remembered.

In 1971, the suite of rooms on the first floor of the Palazzo Guidi was acquired by the Browning Institute. Restoration began, with the eventual aim of refurnishing the drawing room, a romantic literary sanctum recorded by the painter Mignaty after Elizabeth's death in 1861. The familiar writer's clutter of books and paper-burdened tables was here given a grand setting, of richly carved furniture and Renaissance paintings, mingled with comfortable sofas and arm-chairs, all bought by the Brownings with the excitement of a quite ordinary young married couple.

That a combination of Eton College and the Landmark Trust should come to the rescue when money ran short is not as odd as it seems, if the link of a Browning-scholar Eton beak is revealed. Casa Guidi is now owned by Eton and leased to us. Parties of boys will undergo its civilising influence at intervals but at all other times it will be available for our visitors. The tall main rooms, with graceful eighteenth-century decoration, will be furnished as they were by the two poets. Like them, and like their many guests, you will be able to savour this agreeable quarter of Florence through Casa Guidi windows.

The rooms of Casa Guidi open onto the balcony overhanging this street

Robert Browning's study

The Drawing Room, painted in 1862 by Mignaty

There are two beds on a gallery above the shower rooms

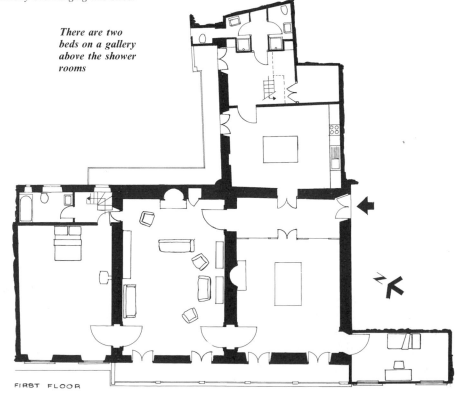

FIRST FLOOR

Causeway House, Bardon Mill, Northumberland

This is the only house in Northumberland still thatched in heather. Known locally as Black Thack, it was of course available in abundant supply, but was seldom used once slate became a cheap alternative in the last century. It survived here because the farmhouse, built around 1800 and never much altered, was abandoned over twenty years ago. Used as a store, its thatch was preserved beneath corrugated iron. Lorry-loads of heather went into its repair, leaving a cover which is thinner and tougher than conventional thatch. Stuffed into holes in the roof we found two dresses, of about 1890, interesting examples of much-worked-in clothing.

Inside, the original arrangement of living room on one side of the cross-wall and byre on the other, with loft over, also survives. The loft is now a warm-weather bedroom, where you can sleep under the knotted tent-like thatch in a fully roofed bed.

The farm, which we own, stands in the rolling, fertile land behind Hadrian's Wall. Past the front runs a Roman Road (a diversion for traffic goes a few feet further off) with the stump

of a Roman milestone nearby; and within a few hundred yards is Vindolanda, where Hadrian's palace has recently been found. Few houses in Britain can have so many traces of Rome around them.

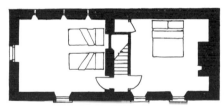

The twin bedroom is unheated, and is therefore not recommended for winter use

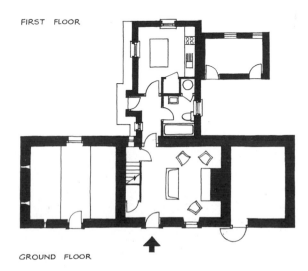

FIRST FLOOR

GROUND FLOOR

17

Cawood Castle, Nr. Selby, Yorkshire

This gatehouse, with the domestic wing to one side of it, is all that remains of Cawood Castle, once a stronghold of the Archbishops of York. It stands in the flat land south of York on the edge of the small town of Cawood, where there is a bridge over the Ouse. By the fifteenth century, when Archbishop Kemple built our richly decorated gatehouse with two well proportioned rooms one over the other, it had become less of a castle and more of a palace; his Cardinal's hat, of which he was proud, appears on several of the finely-carved stone shields over the archway.

Another cardinal to stay here, just once, was Thomas Wolsey: it was here that he was arrested and turned back to the South where he died soon after. Other visitors were Henry III, Edward I and Queen Margaret, Queen Isabella, and Henry VIII and Queen Catherine (Howard)—not all together, of course.

After the Civil War, Cawood was partially dismantled. In the eighteenth century the Gatehouse was used as a courtroom and a respectable Georgian staircase was built to supplement the medieval spiral stair.

It was difficult to save these most historic remains because they were divided between two owners; the domestic wing, long used as a barn, was hidden by derelict farm buildings; and part of the gatehouse was in the adjoining dwelling—the first floor room, with handsome

bay windows at each end, in fact contained a full-size billiard table (how ever did it get there?) manfully supporting during all our long negotiations a huge pile of debris from the collapsed floor above.

In the end our neighbour allowed us to truncate his house a little, and we bought and demolished the farm buildings—so that our visitors can now experience and occupy here a late medieval room of the first quality; and in it, if they like, read some history on the spot where it was made.

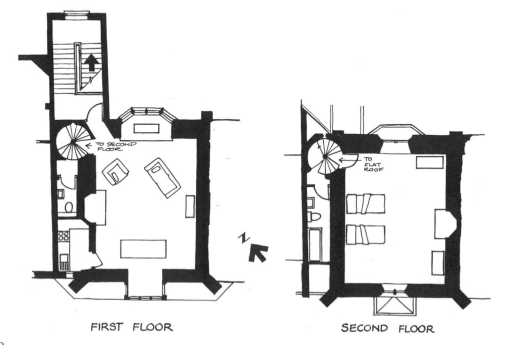

FIRST FLOOR   SECOND FLOOR

The Château, Gate Burton, Lincolnshire

This is the earliest recorded building by John Platt of Rotherham, designed in 1747 when he was 19, and almost his only work outside Yorkshire, where he practised and prospered for the next fifty years.

It stands on a grassy knoll above a big bend of the river Trent, on the edge of Gate Burton park. Built as a Gainsborough lawyer's weekend retreat, and later used for picnics and other mild kinds of excursion, it had since been altered and then neglected. Its present owner gave us a long lease of it.

We have restored the Château to its original elaborate and slightly French appearance. John Platt must have been a talented young man, because it is difficult to realise until one is inside just how small the scale of the building is; apart from the principal room upstairs, which has a high coved ceiling, there is little space in which to swing a cat. But there are fine views across the park and up a shining reach of the Trent, along which big slow barges, piling the water in front of them, press on towards an enormous power station whose cooling towers steam majestically in the distance.

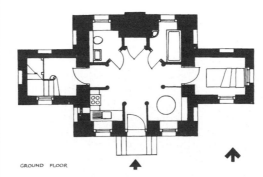

GROUND FLOOR   FIRST FLOOR

Church Cottage, Llandygwydd, Cardiganshire

Church Cottage is early Victorian, modestly Gothic, and made of Cilgerran slate. In 1857 the church itself was rebuilt by R. J. Withers, a prolific architect and committed Ecclesiologist. Our cottage was for the caretaker; it stands in a small village east of Cardigan, in a hilly, well-wooded countryside of small farms. It is also the first building we ever tackled.

Though less than a mile from the main Newcastle Emlyn to Cardigan road, Llandygwydd is extremely quiet; there is, in fact, a small road between the cottage and the church, but little goes along it. Plays in Cardigan Guildhall are recommended; so are the coracle races on the Teifi. The south sweep of Cardigan Bay is less than ten miles away; however the point of Church Cottage is not to dash about, but simply to be there, in this distant and unremarkable part of Wales, and feel what it is like.

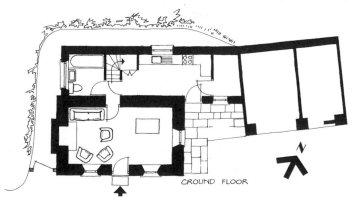

FIRST FLOOR

CROUND FLOOR

From the logbook

"We found lots and lots to do and never strayed outside a five mile radius from the house. Super walks and we managed to wangle a go in a coracle one evening".

"We brought our dinghy and sailed on most days in Cardigan Estuary".

"It was a joy to see hart's tongue ferns growing in the bank outside the bathroom window".

"Very nice indeed, just sit and listen".

Church House, Baltonsborough, Somerset

This is a rare example of a church house which has remained in the ownership, and use, of the parish. We have been brought in to preserve the link, but to take on its care. Built like most such buildings around 1500, on the edge of the churchyard, it has long served Baltonsborough for meetings and festivals, both formal and convivial.

We have made some improvements to the parish room on the ground floor, which still has its great hearth across one end, and continues to serve its original function. Above, in the part you will stay in, is a long room with an open arch-braced roof. The Tudor churchwardens exercised great economy in their building works: no timber is heavier than it need be. Probably for the same reason, when this floor was later fitted out for a tenant, the alterations were minimal, and undamaging.

An old oak partition divides the room, but does not rise to its full height. We plan to leave it like this, so that from your bed at one end your eye can follow the full run of six trusses. From the windows there is a fine view of the church itself. This is entirely fifteenth century

and is dedicated to St. Dunstan, Abbot of Glastonbury and Archbishop of Canterbury in the reign of Edgar the Peaceable. Under Dunstan's patronage, art and learning flourished, and after his death he was chosen as our first patron saint.

The view from the bed

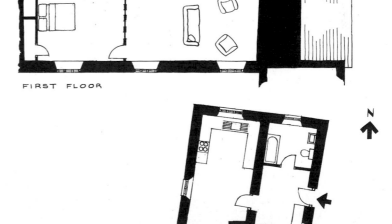

St. Dunstan and the Devil

FIRST FLOOR

GROUND FLOOR

43 & 45a Cloth Fair, Smithfield, London EC1

These plain Georgian houses over shops face the churchyard of St. Bartholomew the Great, which almost alone among City churches escaped the Great Fire of 1666. They were sold to us by the late Paul Paget, who had rescued them many years before, with No. 41, the only remaining house in the City built before the Fire. Round the corner is Smithfield market with its robust architecture, sights and smells, facing the noble buildings of St. Bartholomew's Hospital. Further along Cloth Fair are new houses, bringing domestic life to this part of the City.

There is here a lingering feel of how the whole City of London once was before it was destroyed by money, fire and war—a place where long-established institutions, trades, houses and markets were mingled together. Each of our houses has a respectable staircase, pleasant rooms, and nice old joinery. No. 43 was long the home of Sir John Betjeman.

No. 45a

SECOND FLOOR

SECOND FLOOR

No. 45a FIRST FLOOR

No. 43 FIRST FLOOR

22

Clytha Castle, Nr. Abergavenny, Gwent

'Erected in the year 1790 by William Jones of Clytha House, husband of Elizabeth, last surviving child of Sir William Morgan of Tredegar, it was undertaken with the purpose of relieving a mind afflicted by the loss of a most excellent wife, to the memory of whose virtues this tablet is dedicated'.

This most affecting folly, which we lease from the National Trust, stands on the summit of a small hill, at the edge of a grove of old chestnuts. It was designed by a little known architect and garden designer, John Davenport, perhaps with help from his client. Besides being an eye-catcher, the castle was used for grand picnics, and as a retreat; the square tower contains fine rooms on both floors. When we arrived it had been empty for 25 years and before that had housed a game-keeper. It has the air of a place that has been both loved and neglected. We hope that once again it will relieve the minds of those who come here.

From the logbook

"The children bought a cheap pillowcase (15p) at Abergavenny market and out of this made a flag. The pole is still up on the battlements for future occupants to use".

"Three buzzards soared over the castle for ten minutes this morning".

"Our intentions were to dine out every night, but the atmosphere of the dining room was too much to resist".

"We have enjoyed awakening to the cawing of the rooks and going to sleep listening to the owls calling".

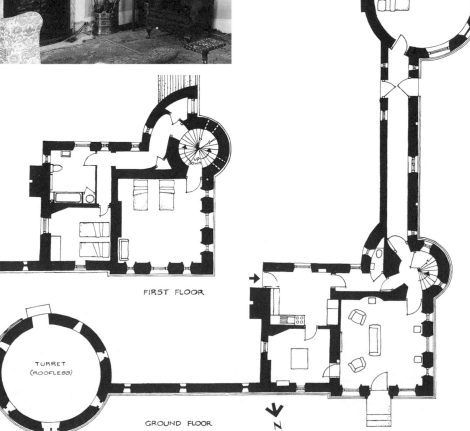

FIRST FLOOR

TURRET (ROOFLESS)

GROUND FLOOR

N

The College, Week St. Mary, Cornwall

When we looked at this house, on the suggestion of one of our visitors, it quickly became clear that it is only part of something that was once much larger, fragments of which are built into the walls and outbuildings around it. These, it turned out, are the remains of a remarkable school, almost the first to be founded by a woman.

Moreover the woman who founded it, Thomasine Bonaventure, was herself remarkable. Though born here in Cornwall, she married, in turn, three London merchants, each of whom died leaving her his property. This she gave or left to charity, amongst many other benefactions founding in 1506 this school at the place of her birth.

To oversee the building work, Thomasine appointed her first cousin, John Dinham of Wortham, twelve miles away (see p. 146). He remodelled his own house at about the same time, and the two buildings have much in common—notably their carved granite doorways.

Unfortunately Thomasine also laid it down that the master (with an Oxford or a Cambridge degree, and six weeks holiday a year) should pray for the souls of her husbands; and so, although the school was said in 1546 to be 'a great comfort to all the country there', it was, as a chantry, dissolved two years later. Thus the

College at Week St. Mary, one of the oldest English schools, prosperously founded, survives only in its name, which still clings to this house more than three hundred years later.

The College faces a small courtyard off the village street. Behind it a meadow slopes down to a chequer-work of little fields, and over them appears, black and afar, the high outline of Dartmoor, beyond which Thomasine ventured to such purpose.

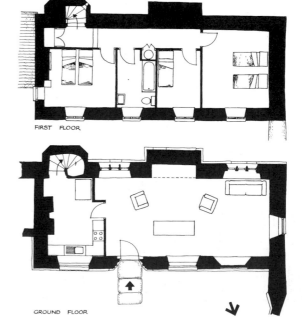

FIRST FLOOR

GROUND FLOOR

Coombe, Nr. Morwenstow, North Cornwall

Coombe consists of a watermill, the mill house, and several cottages, built among orchards round a ford on a shallow stream. It is at the junction of two wooded valleys and is half a mile from the sea at Duckpool, where a sandy beach is exposed at half tide.

Although a small and humble place, Coombe has greatness behind it, since it is where the Grenville family came from. They owned Coombe and lived at Stowe Barton, a few hundred yards up the hill. Interesting traces remain of this great house, demolished in 1739.

Coombe is also partly in the parish of Morwenstow, whose most famous vicar, the Rev. Stephen Hawker, lived here for a short time. He was the inventor (or perhaps reviver) of harvest festivals, and a moving spirit in the saving of life at sea. The Rev. Sabine Baring-Gould ('Onward Christian Soldiers') wrote a life of Hawker. We have managed to get enough copies of this book, by one famous and unusual parson about another, to put one in most of the cottages at Coombe.

We acquired the whole hamlet as part of a joint scheme with the National Trust to preserve it and its exceptional setting. It is a sheltered place, lying well back from the sea.

Almost all the surrounding land, including much of the coast (geologically one of the most impressive in Britain), belongs to the National Trust. There are long and excellent walks in all directions. There are trout in the stream; one visitor tickled and ate nine. The Mill itself, still with all its machinery, is a handsome and interesting stone building with a fine wheel.

The Mill

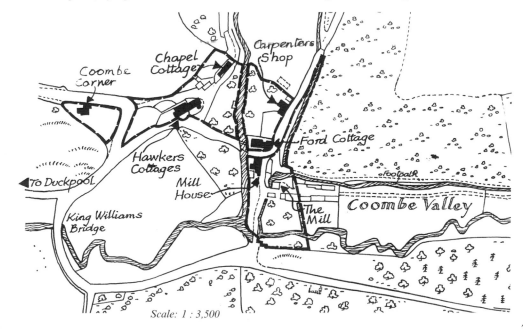

Scale: 1 : 3,500

Rethatching Hawkers Cottages

25

Coombe

The Carpenter's Shop was originally the estate workshop, left derelict for many years. It is a handsome stone building with a spare, functional interior—a large living room open to the roof and two bedrooms leading off a gallery, reached by a spiral stair. The living-room has a slate floor and an open fire, formerly the forge. The doors open straight onto a large old orchard leading down to the stream.

Chapel Cottage is a nineteenth century mission room, of slate and weather-board with sash windows. For some reason, perhaps fiscal, it was originally built on wheels which are still visible under the front. It had been rather brutally enlarged and altered over the years, but we restored the mission room itself and improved the appearance, and interior, of the addition. It is very well placed—a little above the rest of Coombe, looking across the valley over the top of one of the orchards.

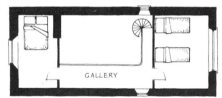

GALLERY

FIRST FLOOR

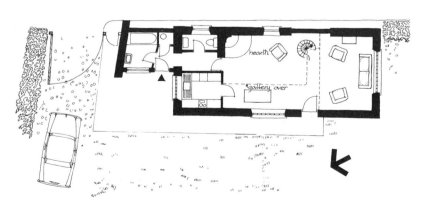

GROUND FLOOR

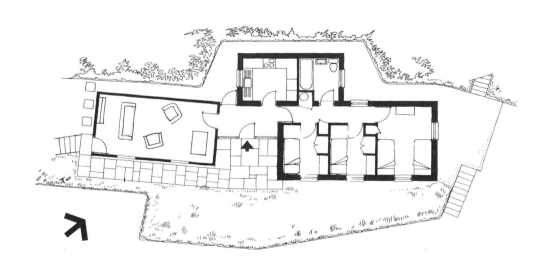

hearth

gallery over

Coombe Corner is a white, weather-boarded bungalow of the 1920s which we bought to round off our ownership of Coombe. It is of good quality and redolent of its period, with a wide view of the valley from high above the rest of the village. From it no other house is visible in any direction.

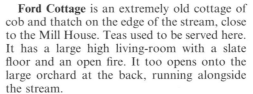

Ford Cottage is an extremely old cottage of cob and thatch on the edge of the stream, close to the Mill House. Teas used to be served here. It has a large high living-room with a slate floor and an open fire. It too opens onto the large orchard at the back, running alongside the stream.

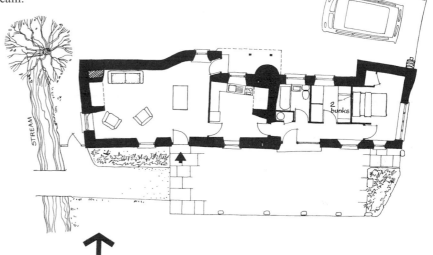

Coombe

Hawkers Cottages are a pair of stone, cob and thatched cottages, called after the famous Vicar of Morwenstow who lived here briefly. The bedroom with a window in the form of a cross, in No. 1, is said to have been his study. No. 2 is slightly larger, and has a handsome living room with a polished slate floor and a particularly splendid old cupboard. The small gardens in front of both cottages are sheltered and pretty.

No. 1

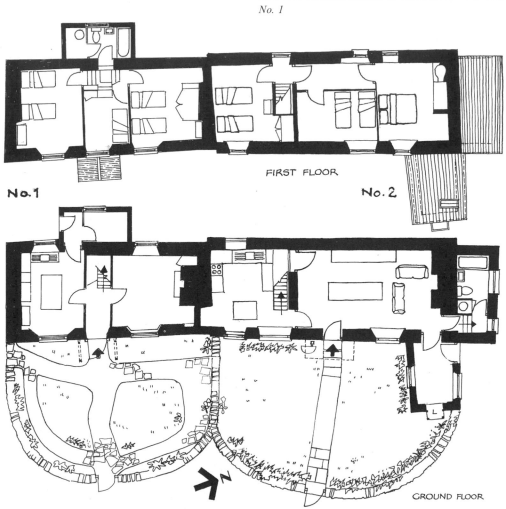

No. 1

FIRST FLOOR

No. 2

GROUND FLOOR

No. 2

28

The Mill House is built of stone and cob with a thatched and slated roof, and is divided into two. The shallow stream runs past a cobbled terrace at the back. One bedroom in each part of the house looks down the valley towards the sea at Duckpool.

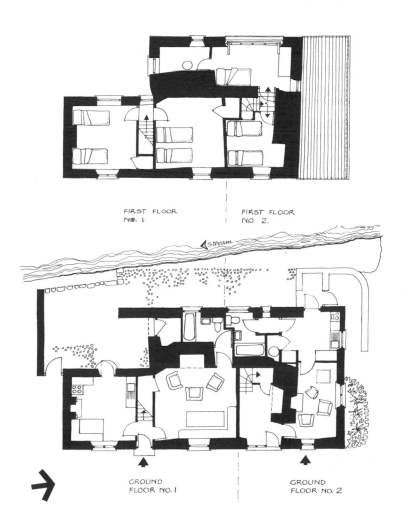

FIRST FLOOR NO. 1.

FIRST FLOOR NO. 2.

GROUND FLOOR NO. 1

GROUND FLOOR NO. 2

The Culloden Tower, Richmond, Yorkshire

This tower was built in 1746 by John Yorke, M.P. for Richmond, to mark the final establishment of Hanoverian rule. It stands in the park of his long demolished house, at the edge of a steep slope above the river Swale, on the site of an old pele tower. It was probably designed by Daniel Garrett (see p. 7).

Inside are to be found, one above the other, two tall octagonal rooms, flooded with daylight and of the highest quality. The carving and plasterwork of the lower is in a Gothick style, while that of the upper is Classical. Here you will sleep under what must be our grandest bedroom ceiling, worth all the sixty steps you must climb to reach it.

Neglect and vandals had done a great deal of damage by the time we bought the tower, but old photographs and salvaged fragments made restoration possible. It is difficult to imagine, certainly to find, a more romantic situation, looking over the trees of this park with the sight and sound of the Swale hurrying over its rocks and stones below; and with the particularly

handsome town of Richmond, which has an eighteenth century theatre and much more besides, a few hundred yards away.

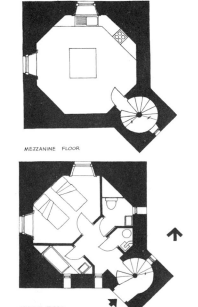

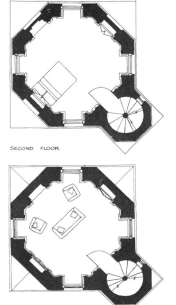

MEZZANINE FLOOR

SECOND FLOOR

GROUND FLOOR

FIRST FLOOR

The Danescombe Mine, Calstock, Cornwall

These are the monumental buildings of the old Cotehele Consols copper and arsenic mine. They are unusually well built, handsome, and complete, and stand by a stream in a steep wooded valley leading down to the Tamar. We have taken a long lease of them from the National Trust and have consolidated and repaired them, so that it is now possible to stay here, in comfort but not luxury, and study at close quarters the tremendous past of the Devon and Cornish mines. It was a dreadful but romantic trade which enriched among others the Dukes of Bedford and the family of William Morris.

The engine house, which we have made habitable, is strongly built of the Killas stone in which the lodes occur, and contained a rotary beam engine with a forty inch cylinder driving a Taylor roll crusher, a pump, and two buddles on the dressing floor. The mine worked, on and off, from 1822 to 1900, kept alive at the last by the demand for arsenic to protect cotton against the boll weevil. In the woods above lie the abandoned shafts of other mines; and only a short and beautiful walk away above the Tamar, is Cotehele, a most notable medieval house.

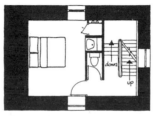

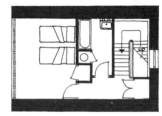

FIRST FLOOR

SECOND FLOOR

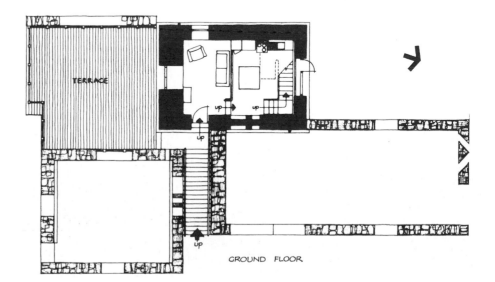

TERRACE

GROUND FLOOR

The East Banqueting House, Chipping Campden, Gloucestershire

In 1613 the newly-enriched Sir Baptist Hicks began work on a house in Chipping Campden. It was a noble work in the latest fashion, with intricate gardens. Thirty years later it was destroyed, wantonly, by the Royalists, when in 1645 they withdrew from the town. 'The house (which was so faire) burnt', noted one, sadly.

Only a shell was left, now shrunk to a single fragment. But other, lesser, buildings escaped the fire, and are still there, together with the raised walks of the garden. The ogee domes of the lodges are well known, but in the field beyond are two banqueting houses with ebullient strapwork parapets. One of these, we have leased from the present owner descendant of Sir Baptist, together with the lodges.

Our banqueting house stands at the end of the broad main terrace that ran along the garden front of the house, and its fine upper room opens directly onto this. Here the family came at the end of the main meal, to drink rare wines and eat fruit and small cakes and sweetmeats, while enjoying the outlook over the garden. Below are two further storeys, once self-contained and hidden from above by the fall of the ground.

To get here you must walk along a grassy path, leaving your car by the lodges. From there on you will be alone with the site of this great house. Whether you nibble the crystallized petals of a flower, and sip Tokay, or make do with fish and chips and beer, in this place it must surely taste sublime.

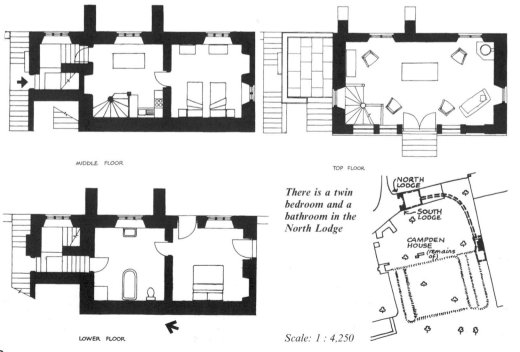

MIDDLE FLOOR

TOP FLOOR

LOWER FLOOR

There is a twin bedroom and a bathroom in the North Lodge

NORTH LODGE

SOUTH LODGE

CAMPDEN HOUSE (remains of)

Scale: 1 : 4,250

Edale Mill, Edale, Derbyshire

This cotton mill was built in the late eighteenth century, and during the whole of its long working life survived the hazards of finance and fire, to both of which such mills were prone. After 1800 it was extended at each end and the stone staircase tower was added. When the Manchester to Sheffield railway was built through the Hope valley in the 1890s it became practicable to use coal; the water wheel was removed and the mill was powered by steam until its then owners, Fine Spinners and Doublers Ltd., closed it in 1934.

We bought it in 1969, restored the slate roof and every single window, and divided the interior into seven dwellings, six of which we sold and one of which, on the second floor, we kept as a Landmark. Our architect took particular trouble with such details as the downpipes, which were specially made for us square in section, making all the difference to the mill's appearance; and we put the telephone and electricity underground. In spite of these apparent extravagances the whole project turned out

to be economic and the mill, instead of being demolished, now remains, we hope, an ornament to the dale and a monument to those who laboured in it.

From the logbook

"We went for a long walk, twelve miles or so, through Edale village, up the stream to the moor and along it to the Roman track . . . hot sunshine and no wind all day long. Many grouse close enough to see clearly".

"You do recover from a twenty mile walk".

"The days were bright and clear and the night's freezing—I've never seen so many stars".

"The right combination of luxury and puritanism".

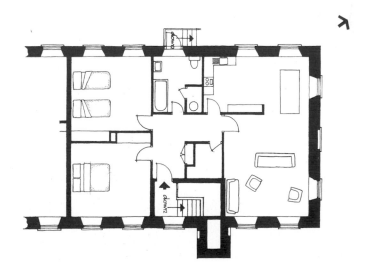

The Landmark flat is at the right hand end of the mill building, on the second floor

The Egyptian House, Chapel Street, Penzance, Cornwall

This is a rare and noble survivor of a style which enjoyed a vogue after Napoleon's campaign in Egypt of 1798. It dates from about 1835 and the front elevation is very similar to that of the former Egyptian Hall in Piccadilly, designed in 1812 by P. F. Robinson. Robinson and Foulston of Plymouth are the most likely candidates for its design, but there is no evidence to support the claim of either.

It was built for John Lavin as a museum and geological repository. Behind its colossal facade with lotus bud capitals and enrichments of Coade stone lay, when we bought it in 1968, two small granite houses above shops, solid and with a pleasant rear elevation, but very decrepit inside. These in the course of our work to the front, we reconstructed as three flats, the highest of which has a fine view of Mounts Bay and St. Michael's Mount.

Why was there a geological shop here? Although picked over by the Victorians (doubtless including Mr Lavin) the beaches at Penzance hold every kind of pebble, from quartz to chalcedony. Penzance itself, accessible by train, is a handsome and agreeable town; and beyond it lies that hard old peninsula in which, at places like Chysauster and the Botallack mine, can be found moving evidences of human labour, over an immense span of time.

From the logbook

". . . windows with views of St. Michael's Mount, a lighthouse, a church clock with a flat chime, seagulls seen through the skylights, an elliptical staircase, and a barrel organ in the street".

"Perfect place to be when writing a book as I was".

"Penzance is worth exploring, far more so than prettified St. Ives".

"On Sunday morning you can take a boat from Penzance Harbour to St. Michael's Mount for the service in the chapel".

"We much appreciated the furniture and delighted in the witty Egyptian motifs".

"Found a sleepy snake, a man picking daffodils and a farmer who sold us one of his cauliflowers."

We were entranced by the flat especially the curved front door."

"Its always a pleasure to be here in Penzance – it's such a happy place."

"...Much praise, particularly for the choice of books."

Three flats, for 3, 4 and 4 people

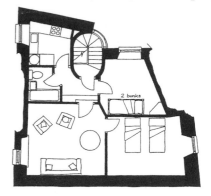

THIRD FLOOR

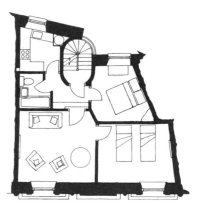

SECOND FLOOR

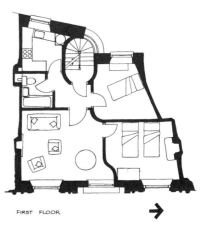

FIRST FLOOR

Endsleigh, Nr. Tavistock, Devon

This most naturally beautiful stretch of the River Tamar (Turner, among others, sketched here and called it 'altogether Italian') was chosen by Georgiana, Duchess of Bedford, as the setting for a new house; both Repton and Wyatville played a part in shaping it to perfection, and in placing suitable buildings within it. Endsleigh today is still a very complete example of that most imaginative and English taste, the Picturesque. Most of it now belongs to a fishing syndicate; they use the main house, the Cottage, as a fishing lodge-cum-hotel, and have done much to restore the garden and arboretum.

Other parts of the woods were sold separately, and it was inevitable that unfunctional buildings should suffer. So in 1977 we bought **The Swiss Cottage**, perhaps the most important of them. It is an early, and wonderfully well-made, example of the nineteenth century passion for the Alps, designed about 1815 by Jeffry Wyatville, complete with an Alpine garden, and Swiss furniture and crockery. We repaired it and reversed some later alterations, and once again furnished it—but not excessively—*a la*

Suisse. The main room, opening onto a verandah, was always kept by the Dukes for picnics and shooting lunches and there, perched high above the river, you have a heady feeling of surveying a world apart.

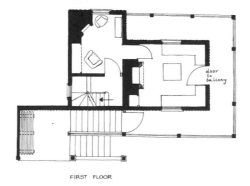

FIRST FLOOR

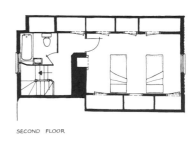

SECOND FLOOR

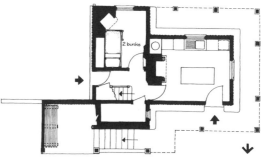

GROUND FLOOR

SWISS COTTAGE

Then in 1983 we took on the Dairy, a strongly Picturesque building, and with it **Pond Cottage**, previously used by visiting fishermen (you too can flyfish in the pond). Both buildings were designed by Wyatville, but the idea for creating 'Dairy Dell', with its streams and cascades, its still dark pond and overhung ancient well, was Repton's, proposed in his *Red Book* for Endsleigh.

Pond Cottage has a Rustic porch, with tree trunk columns and honeysuckle, and cosy rooms. The Dairy, which had to be rescued from the undergrowth, is perched on a knoll above, a cool chamber of marble (a local variety) and ivy-leaf tiles. From its verandah, 'embosomed', as Repton put it, 'in all the sublimity of umbrageous majesty', you may open yourself to those keen responses to the surrounding scene that were so carefully planned by its creators—while contemplating the making of a very superior butter.

Inside the Dairy

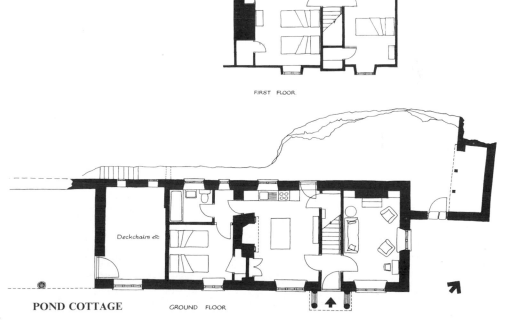

FIRST FLOOR

POND COTTAGE　　GROUND FLOOR

Deckchairs etc

37

Field House, Minchinhampton, Gloucestershire

This handsome stone house was left to us with the surrounding land by Miss Eileen Jenkins, who had lived here for the past twenty years. It is an unusual building, since although it looks like a single house, and indeed has been one for over a century, it was clearly once four separate dwellings round a narrow yard, each with one room up and one down. But by 1884 the yard had been roofed over and filled with a staircase, and the whole building became one farmhouse.

The thick party walls of the old dwellings give Field House a pleasant, solid feel inside. It stands in a large and sheltered walled garden (still cared for by Miss Jenkins' gardener) high up on the top of the Cotswolds, once a land of sheep but now more given over to the horse.

From the logbook

"We were made very welcome by the ringers in Minchinhampton who practice on Friday evenings (6 bells). We were even asked to ring at a wedding the following day—very profitable".

"In Cheltenham . . . dress very smartly if you want to pass off as a local".

"We have played hide and seek, treasure hunts, rested on the lawn, threatened children with the cellar, ignored the outside world, and fallen in love with Field House".

"One of the nicest things has been closing the shutters at night and then opening them again in the morning to enjoy the sense of space around the house".

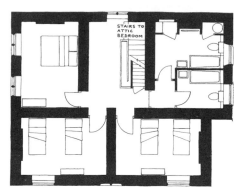

FIRST FLOOR

There is a single bedroom in the attic (not shown)

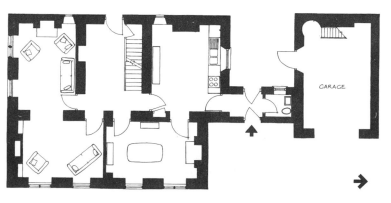

GROUND FLOOR

38

Fox Hall, Charlton, West Sussex

Charlton is just a small village, but at one time, when the Charlton Hunt was famous and fashionable, its name was familiar and dear to every sportsman in England. Even Goodwood was described as 'near Charlton'. The hunt was founded in 1670s by the Duke of Monmouth and was continued after his death by his son-in-law the Duke of Bolton; and then by the Duke of Richmond.

Apart from the sport, what attracted high-spirited noblemen here, surely, was that they could live in lodgings away from the constraints of home. They clubbed together and built for themselves a dining room which they christened 'Fox Hall', designed by Lord Burlington, no less, and here 'these votaries of Diana feasted after the chase and recounted the feats of the day'. Not to miss such affairs and to be in good time for the meets, the Duke of Richmond put up for himself in 1730 the small Palladian building which we now possess. The designer of this rich sample of architecture was most probably Lord Burlington's assistant Roger Morris.

It consists of a plain brick box with a small stylish hall and staircase leading to one magnificent room above, undoubtedly Britain's premier bed-sitter. There is a gilded alcove for the Duke's bed and in the pediment over the fireplace an indicator shows the direction of the wind, important information for the fox hunter. The front door to all this grandeur leads very sensibly straight to the stable yard.

In the 1750s the Hunt was moved away from Charlton to Goodwood. The old Fox Hall disappeared and somehow its name was transferred to our building a few yards off, which, grievously altered, for a long time housed the manager of the Duke of Richmond's sawmill. So far as possible we have given it back its original form.

Apart from Fox Hall, and a detail or two in some of the houses, no visible trace now remains at Charlton of the famous Hunt; but the pub is called the Fox, a modest clue to great doings here in former times.

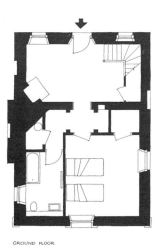

GROUND FLOOR

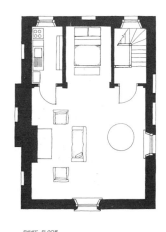

FIRST FLOOR

39

Fort Clonque, Alderney, Channel Islands

In the 1840s it was thought that the advent of steam would make the Channel Islands more important as an advanced naval base, and also more liable to capture by the French. Accordingly the great harbour works of Alderney were begun in 1847. Fort Clonque, the most remarkable of them, occupies a group of large rocks off the steep south-west tip of the island, commanding the passage between it and Burhou. It is reached by a causeway and was originally designed for ten 64-pounder guns in four open batteries, manned by two officers and fifty men.

Very soon however the further development of steam brought the Channel Islands within easy reach of mainland bases, and made another in Alderney unnecessary. In 1886, the Defence Committee recommended that Clonque and all the other works except Fort Albert should be disarmed, but left standing.

It was thus that Hitler found them in 1940 and, imagining again that the Channel Islands had strategic value, vigorously refortified them. At Fort Clonque, part of the Victorian soldiers'

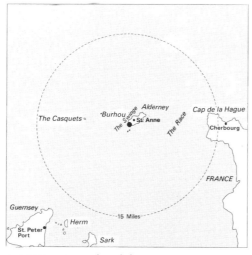

quarters was replaced by an enormous casemate, housing a gun so large that its emplacement now makes a handsome bedroom looking towards Guernsey.

Most forts are of necessity large and grim, but Clonque, because it has had to be fitted to the great rocks round which it is built, is small, open and picturesque, ingeniously contrived on many levels with stretches of grass, samphire and mesembryanthemum here and there. The clean air allows all sorts of lichen to grow on the granite walls. On calm days the sea can be heard all round, restlessly searching the rocks; and on rough days it is comforting to reflect that the wall of the East Flank Battery is nineteen feet thick. At high tide the fort is cut off and the sea runs between it and the mainland.

All the time there is a marine view second to none—of the other islands, rocks and stacks; of two great colonies of gannets, which fish round the fort; of the lighthouses on the Casquets; and of the formidable race or current called the Swinge which runs between Clonque and Burhou. On all counts, Fort Clonque is a most worthwhile place to have tackled, not least

because when we embarked on it in 1966 military works such as this were disregarded everywhere.

The rest of Alderney is also extremely pleasant; the island is just small enough to be explored entirely on foot or, very easily, by bicycle; all the Victorian and German defence works are interesting; the beaches at the north end are exceptional; and in the centre is St. Anne, a very pretty little town, English with a hint of France.

From the logbook

"Our attempts to sound Reveille and Come to the Cookhouse Door on the thoughtfully provided bugle gave hours of harmless fun."

"Acoustics in the kitchen are ideal for singing and lute music."

"The cycling in Alderney is fabulous."

"I found a bread and butter sea slug; it looked positively revolting."

"The fort is a marvellous novelty."

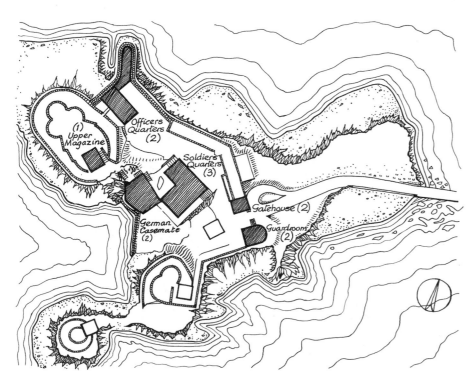

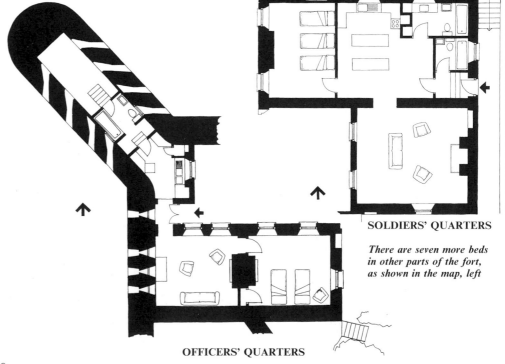

SOLDIERS' QUARTERS

There are seven more beds in other parts of the fort, as shown in the map, left

OFFICERS' QUARTERS

Frenchman's Creek, Helford, Cornwall

You can see small, granite cottages like this in their hundreds in Cornwall, but it would be hard to find one in a more remote, romantic, and secluded place than this, tucked down at the head of Frenchman's Creek on the Helford River. It was built about 1840 for a farm worker or boatman; there were once two more cottages here and a small quay. Between the Wars, it was rented as a retreat by Maria Pendragon and Clara Vyvyan, who describes it in her book *The Helford River*. The last inhabitants moved out a few years ago, and the National Trust, which owns the land around, suggested a joint scheme to us, as the only alternative to letting it fall down.

The Creek, one of many along the shores of the tidal River, runs like a finger deep into the woods, giving brief sparkling glimpses of water between the trees—and at high tide it is passable by boat. The path down to the cottage is steep (and sometimes slippery, you may prefer to leave your car at the top); in summer, for the woods are mainly oak, you descend into greenness, with the light filtered through leaves. It is a place for those who worship the woods and

the water, and are prepared to be temporarily dominated by them. Should you want to go elsewhere, there is the Lizard to explore, and Mounts Bay, or to the east, the granite elegance of Falmouth.

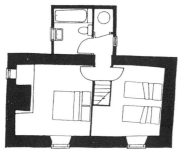

FIRST FLOOR

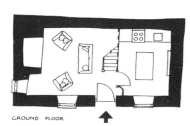

GROUND FLOOR

42

The Gothic Temple, Stowe, Buckinghamshire

This temple, built in 1741, is one of the last additions to the garden formed for Lord Cobham at Stowe by Charles Bridgeman and his successor, William Kent. That same year, 'Capability' Brown arrived as gardener, to begin his own transformation of the landscape.

Lord Cobham dedicated his new temple, designed by James Gibbs, 'to the Liberty of our Ancestors', for which the Gothic style was deemed appropriate. Inside, the rooms are all circular, with moulded stone pilasters and plaster vaults—the main vault of the central space being gorgeously painted with heraldry. To be on the first floor gallery is an important architectural experience; and at the top of the staircase there is a belvedere with stone seats and a fine view over this former demesne of Lord Cobham and his successors—of which the National Trust is now guardian.

Stowe School gave us a long lease of the temple in 1970. It does have all modern conveniences, if in rather surprising places, and the heating has to work hard to be noticed; but we hope that the splendour of the temple and its surroundings will compensate those who stay here.

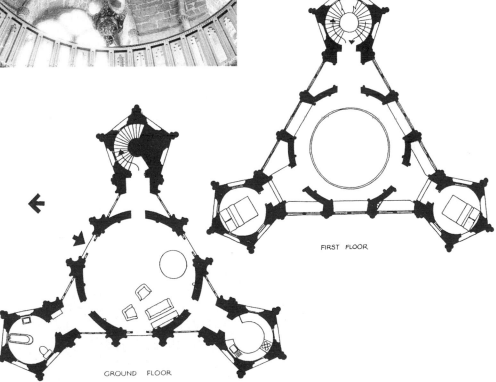

FIRST FLOOR

GROUND FLOOR

The Grammar School, Kirby Hill, Yorkshire

Built in the discouraging reign of Queen Mary, this is one of a group of stone-roofed buildings which surround the airy village green of Kirby Hill. The Trust which owns the school was founded by Dr. Dakyn on the 11th May 1556. After Mass he explained to a numerous congregation how the Wardens of the Trust were to be chosen. On the feast of the Decollation of St. John the names of six respectable parishioners were to be written on slips of paper, and enclosed in balls of wax. These were to be put into a jar of water. Two names were then to be drawn and the jar of water with the remaining names put away in a cupboard which he also provided. If a vacancy occurred during the year, a further ball of wax was to be drawn from the jar and opened. This is still done, and the jar is still kept in his cupboard, a very handsome one.

In 1957, after a life of 401 years, his school was closed and in 1973 the Trustees gave us a long lease of it. We repaired the ground floor schoolroom for use as a village hall, and the Tudor lodging of the master, upstairs, we turned into a flat. It has one particularly fine bedroom, looking into the churchyard. There is a large library of old school books (in the building when we arrived) and a general atmosphere of ancient peace, abetted by the church clock with its tranquillising strike.

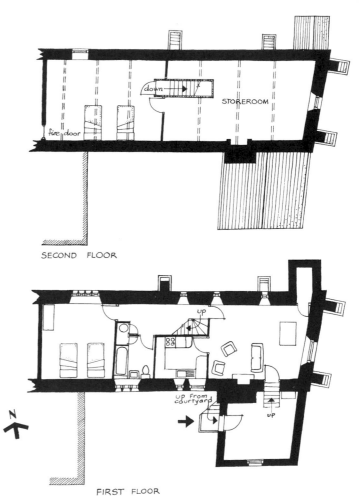

SECOND FLOOR

FIRST FLOOR

The Landmark flat is in the range set back on the right with the large chimney

Gurney Manor, Cannington, Somerset

When we first saw Gurney Manor it was divided into seven run-down flats. It is a mainly late medieval manor house built, unusually, round a courtyard. Apart from the hall roof, which was renewed about 1900, and Tudor windows and fireplaces in the adjoining solar block, the best medieval work survives unaltered, including a tiny oratory and a pentice, or covered passage, across the yard.

The man responsible for this was, as often, a lawyer, William Dodisham, son of a Gurney daughter. His heirs, the Mitchells, faded out before the Civil War and life thereafter as a tenant farm kept the house from major rebuilding. In the 1940s it was bought by a local developer who divided it up into flats.

We have returned the house to its original undivided state. Its repair took eight years, carried out by a small team under the careful and knowledgeable eye of our foreman, Philip Ford. New collar trusses were made in the traditional way, from single pieces of oak shaped with an adze. The walls are rendered with lime plaster, buffered to a thinness equal to that achieved by medieval craftsmen.

The medieval house in its final and most fully developed form, with its balance of private and communal rooms, was a comfortable and convenient one. There can be few better ways of learning this than by staying here, in this tranquil and enclosed place. Cannington is a pleasant town not far from the Quantocks, with an excellent nursery garden.

Gurney Manor

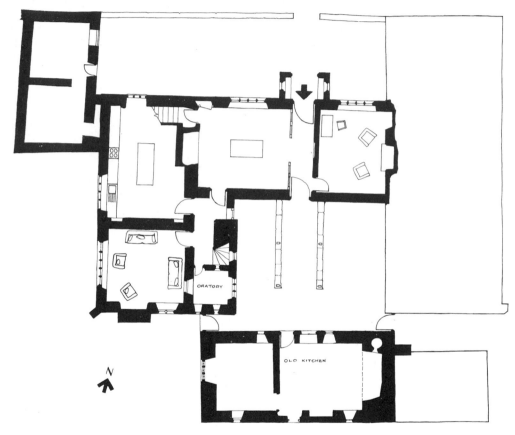

GROUND FLOOR

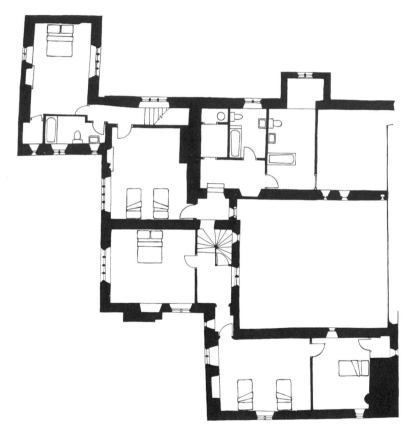

FIRST FLOOR

Hampton Court Palace, East Molesey, Surrey

Hampton Court Palace is no empty museum, but a large and thriving community, following a tradition set by George III, who allowed loyal servants to live here by Grace and Favour. Now home mainly to institutions, and a few residents, the sense of a secret life beyond the public eye survives—of doors leading to invisible corridors, of figures disappearing up a staircase with briefcase or shopping basket.

The opportunity we offer our visitors, on behalf of Historic Royal Palaces, is to become part of this life, to go past the security barrier, to make yourself at home in a palace. Hampton Court is so much a part of our history that it needs no new introduction. The details are best learned there, slowly and at first hand: our visitors are free to explore the gardens and most of the courtyards at all times, early and late, and the public rooms of the palace during opening hours.

Hampton Court has always been loved. Ernest Law, its chief historian, wrote, 'There is something so essentially home-like in the old Palace, that very few can dwell within it long, without growing attached to it'. Alexander

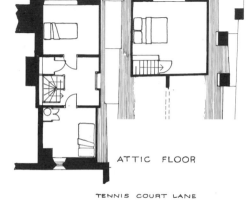

Pope, visiting in 1718, was entranced: 'No lone house in Wales is more contemplative than Hampton Court. I walked there the other day by the moon, and met no creature of quality but the King, who was giving audience all alone to the birds under the garden wall'.

This apartment, with its front door in **Fish Court**, was originally for the Officers of the Pastry. It is in the service wing of the Tudor palace. Begun by Cardinal Wolsey, this was enlarged by Henry VIII, who entertained even more lavishly, and added new kitchens, one entirely for the baking of pies. The windows look south over Master Carpenter's Court and north towards Bushy Park.

ATTIC FLOOR

TENNIS COURT LANE

FIRST FLOOR

The Georgian House

Fish Court

48

The alternative is to stay in **The Georgian House**, an imposing building just north of the palace. It looks like a garrison commander's house, but was in fact a kitchen built in 1719 for George, Prince of Wales. Its near-twin at St. James's Palace is thought to be by Vanbrugh. Later, it became two houses, for the Clerk of Works and the Gardener. You will stay in the eastern one, with a private walled garden, into which the morning sun shines. The main rooms are handsome, the attics have a fine view of the palace roofs, and in the kitchen is a huge blocked arch, once a Royal cooking hearth.

There is a twin bedroom, a single bedroom and a bathroom on the second floor

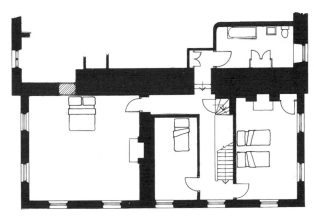

FIRST FLOOR

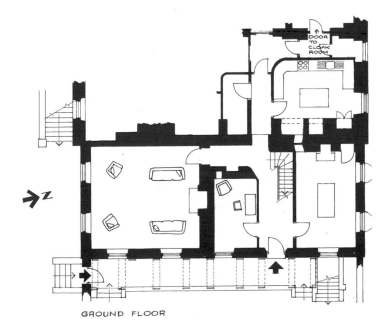

GROUND FLOOR

49

34 High Street, Ironbridge, Shropshire

The sale particulars said: 'These premises have been occupied by the Firm of Messrs. Egerton Smith & Sons for many years. They were specially built, at a great cost, by the late Mr Smith and occupy a Unique Position in Ironbridge.' They certainly do—unique in the world, overlooking that harbinger of our age, forerunner and survivor, the Iron Bridge.

No. 34 is the complete establishment of a substantial grocer, with a large house over a double-fronted shop, and all the offices behind, from store rooms to stables. From the cellars a tunnel runs to the bank of the River Severn, up which, until the late nineteenth century, the cargoes were brought by barge.

The shop is let to the Ironbridge Gorge Museum Trust. Mr Smith's quarters upstairs we divided in two, one part for a long-term tenant, and the other, on two floors, is where you will stay. The living room has a fine iron fireplace cast here in Coalbrookdale (as was the bathroom basin and lavatory cistern), and this and every other room faces the river, the bridge, and the steep woods beyond. It is a wonderful place to be, with coal smoke drifting against the trees,

and the sun glittering on the rather muddy Severn as it flows inexhaustibly beneath Abraham Darby's iron arch. All around, in Coalport, Ironbridge and Coalbrookdale, are the remains of industry's beginning.

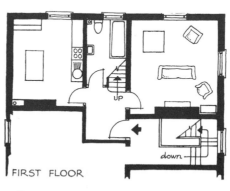

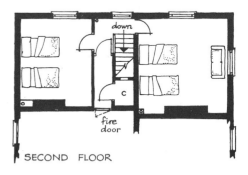

FIRST FLOOR

SECOND FLOOR

The Hill House, Helensburgh, Nr. Glasgow

The Hill House is the domestic masterpiece of the great Scottish architect Charles Rennie Mackintosh. Not particularly successful or lucky, he was an undoubted genius, a product of the flowering of art in Glasgow at the end of the nineteenth century. His influence is still discernible in many buildings and artefacts today. In 1902 he was commissioned by Walter Blackie, the publisher, to design for him this house and everything in it, a bold decision indeed.

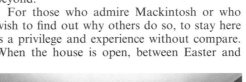

The house (and the British public) has since been very lucky. With much of its original contents, it is now cared for by the National Trust for Scotland. In 1978 we came to the aid of the previous owner, the Royal Incorporation of Architects in Scotland. Bravely departing from its usual role as a professional body, it had in 1972 raised the money to buy the house when no other preservation body would take it on, but had scarce means to maintain it. As well as helping the RIAS directly, we took a lease of the top floor, which had been turned into a flat, and here we remain as tenants.

The principal room of our flat was the schoolroom of the Blackie family. Like all rooms once the domain of children it has the feeling of a place where much spirit and energy have been expended. It is large and irregularly shaped, under the roof, with bookcases (now filled by us with Blackie's Annuals) and toy cupboards designed by Mackintosh—and with a big, three sided bay window, flooded with daylight, looking over the Firth of Clyde and beyond.

For those who admire Mackintosh or who wish to find out why others do so, to stay here is a privilege and experience without compare. When the house is open, between Easter and Christmas, you have free access to it during opening hours; and to the garden at all times.

Helensburgh, on the upper edge of which The Hill House stands, is a pleasant, interesting place. An early and farsighted example of town-planning, it was laid out on very generous lines in 1775. Big houses in big gardens line its broad tree-planted roads. And over the top of the hill is the road to Loch Lomond.

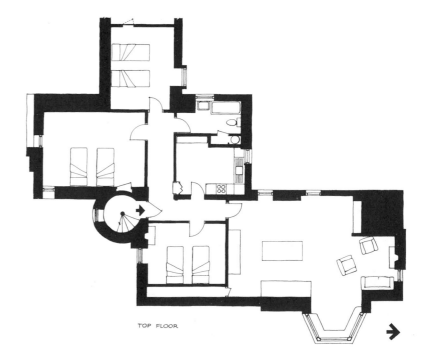

TOP FLOOR

Hole Cottage, Cowden, Kent

This is the cross-wing of a late medieval timber-framed hall-house, of high quality, the rest of which was pulled down in 1833. It lies by a small stream in a woodland clearing, and curiously enough, is easily accessible by railway, since it is only a fifteen minute walk through the wood from Cowden station.

The Hole still has the true feeling of the Weald, and of the deep woods in whose drip and shade the forges and furnaces of the Sussex ironmasters were established. This despite the great storm of October 1987. The logbook records the events of that night as the wind gathered strength: 'At about 3.30 we decided to go down to the sitting room. As we sat with our one candle burning we heard a terrific crash in the big room upstairs: a big tree had fallen right on the peak of the roof. As the night went on trees fell one after another all about the house . . . Mr Dale arrived with a flask of hot water at about 8.30 and a very welcome sight he was'. New trees are growing up fast, to enclose once

again this quiet solitary place, where you may enjoy a sleepy fire, the smell of its smoke, and the sound of the stream.

From the logbook

"It's all green, and suddenly the cottage is standing there as it has been all the time".

"We arrived late by train: the stationmaster guided us through the trees".

"We didn't go anywhere as it is so nice here".

"The landlord of the Kentish Horse has a good strong cider, which he is reluctant to serve to ladies in large quantities".

"Thank you Hole Cottage".

GROUND FLOOR

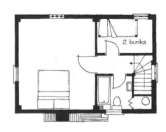

FIRST FLOOR

2 bunks

The House of Correction, Folkingham, Lincolnshire

Folkingham is one of those agreeable places which are less important than they used to be. It has a single very wide street, lined on each side by handsome buildings, with a large eighteenth century inn across the top end. Behind the houses, to the east, lie the moat and earthworks of a big medieval castle. The House of Correction occupies the site of this castle.

These minor prisons were originally intended for minor offenders—the idle (regarded as subversive) and the disorderly. Folkingham had a house of correction by 1611, replaced in 1808 by a new one built inside the castle moat and intended to serve the whole of Kesteven. This was enlarged in 1825 and given a grand new entrance. In 1878 the prison was closed and the inner buildings converted into ten dwellings, all demolished in 1955.

The grand entrance which survives was designed by Bryan Browning, an original and scholarly Lincolnshire architect also responsible for the Sessions House at Bourne. It is a bold and monumental work, borrowing from the styles of Vanbrugh, Sanmichele and Ledoux. Apart from cowing the malefactor it was

intended to house the Turnkey, and the Governor's horses and carriage. Now it gives entrance only to a moated expanse of grass—a noble piece of architecture in a beautiful and interesting place.

From the logbook

"How charming to find, behind the grand portico, something so elegant and snug."

"Anyone who doesn't love their stay here needs to be locked up."

"... the children were particularly taken with the handcuffs."

"We have left a pair of swords to defend yourselves in case of an uprising by the prisoners below."

"Trees good for climbing, moat good for adventure."

"What a pleasure to be an inmate!"

ATTIC

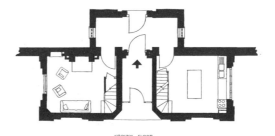

GROUND FLOOR

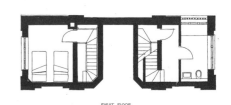

FIRST FLOOR

Howthwaite, Grasmere, Cumbria

The land on which this house stands is immediately behind and above Dove Cottage. Wordsworth used to walk and sit here composing his poems, as his sister Dorothy records in her diary. For that reason, when it was offered for sale, the Trustees of Dove Cottage were anxious that it should fall into friendly hands and asked if we would join with them in buying it.

The house was built in 1926 by Miss Jessie Macdougall, of the family of millers, who bought the land from the Widow of the famous Warden Spooner of New College. Though not great architecture it seemed to us a good, unaltered example of the solid houses put up by those cultivated, well-to-do people who were attracted to the Lake District; the kind of people who, among other things, had prompted the foundation of the National Trust. Certainly its light, airy rooms and fine outlook and surroundings will give pleasure to many, particularly to those who enjoy Wordsworth, and the landscape that inspired him.

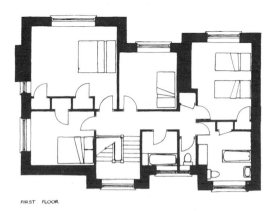

FIRST FLOOR

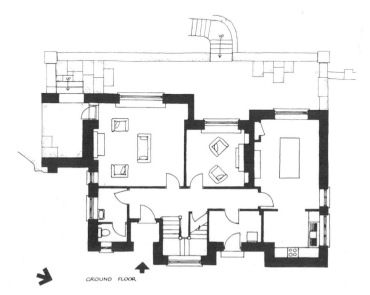

GROUND FLOOR

55

Ingestre Pavilion, Staffordshire

The approach to this building is now from the side along a forest ride, but the long vista from it, between plantations to the Trent, is as it was when Capability Brown drew up a scheme for 'an Intended Lawn' at Ingestre for the 2nd Viscount Chetwynd in 1756. The Pavilion was already there by then, added about 1752 to an earlier, more formal layout.

The façade is a powerful and distinguished one. Curiously, for nearly two centuries it has been little more than that: by 1802 the building behind it, which the foundations show to have been surprisingly large and grand, had been demolished. In its place there are now new rooms designed by Philip Jebb, including a central octagonal saloon.

A local Mason-Architect named Charles Trubshaw (who trained as a sculptor under Scheemakers) worked at Ingestre around 1750, and he probably put up the Pavilion. It is unlikely that he was also its designer, able though he was. The Chetwynds, and after them the Talbots, were enlightened patrons of architecture—the parish church is by Wren—and undoubtedly this is the work of one of the best architects available.

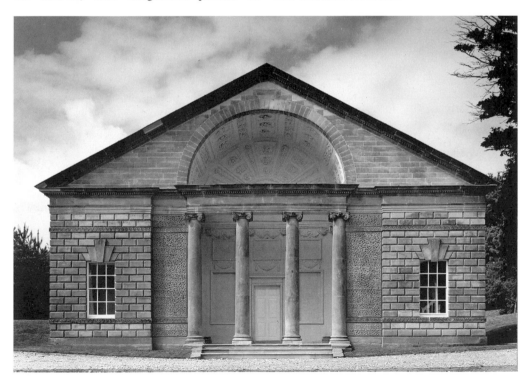

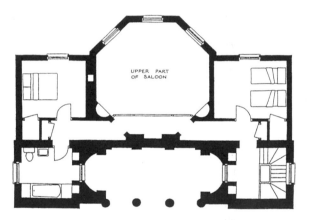

UPPER PART OF SALOON

FIRST FLOOR

GROUND FLOOR

Kingswear Castle, Nr. Dartmouth, South Devon

In 1481 a new castle was begun at Dartmouth, to defend the harbour there. To support it from the opposite shore, Kingswear Castle was completed in 1502. Together they represent the most advanced military design of their day. For the first time large guns, such as murderers and serpyntynes, were mounted inside on the ground floor, with rectangular ports through which to fire them.

Within fifty years, Kingswear was redundant: for another century it was manned in time of war, but thereafter was left to decay, until rescued and turned into a summer residence in 1855 by a rich young bachelor, Charles Seale Hayne. During the last World War, a concrete blockhouse (now a thrilling, if spartan, extra bedroom), was built fifty yards from it.

We have restored the castle's ground floor to look as it did in 1502, with the living quarters above. The rooms have that sense of comfort in an exposed place which the Victorians knew so well how to achieve. The tower stands almost on the water's edge (those with children beware) and its rooms are filled with shifting, reflected

light. From the windows, you can look across to Dartmouth; or down the rocky coast, with its woods of maritime pine, and out to sea. Above all you can watch the river, busy now with friendly shipping.

From the logbook

"Saw the departure of HMS Battleaxe, dipped the Union flag, but she was ready for us and answered before ours was fully at the dip".

"The blockhouse has been the greatest surprise. I'd never imagined it could be such an intriguing place. My first impression was of being inside a submarine".

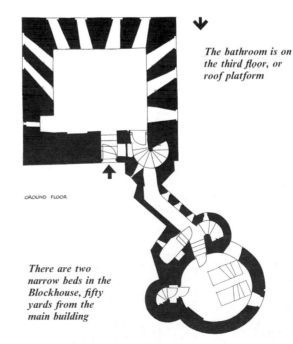

The bathroom is on the third floor, or roof platform

GROUND FLOOR

SECOND FLOOR

STAIRS TO BATHROOM AND ROOF PLATFORM

There are two narrow beds in the Blockhouse, fifty yards from the main building

FIRST FLOOR

Knowle Hill, Nr. Ticknall, Derbyshire

In 1698, Walter Burdett, a younger son born nearby at Foremark, retired from the Middle Temple. On land leased from his friend, Thomas Coke of Melbourne, he built for himself a most curious house on the side of a ravine. Here, being a likeable and sociable person, he entertained his many friends; and around it he formed a garden which, for all its formal structure of terraces and pools, blended evocatively with the natural landscape—remarkably so at that early date.

In the 1760s, the house was pulled down by Walter's great-nephew, but the atmosphere of a woodland retreat was preserved—and the extraordinary grotto at the heart of the garden, from which a tunnel leads to a rock-cut chamber, may have been added. A Gothick summerhouse was built on an upper terrace, overlooking the Trent valley, with a cottage for a custodian behind. Until abandoned in this century, parties came often to walk amid the Picturesque delights of trees and water.

By 1989, Knowle Hill was divided between three owners, but it is now reunited, and the process of revival is under way. We have

repaired the cottage for you to stay in, with the summerhouse as your drawing room. It opens onto a sunny lawn, with a view into the woods beyond and, if you are lucky, a glimpse of water foaming over a cascade: an ideal world, realised enchantingly in miniature.

West range from above

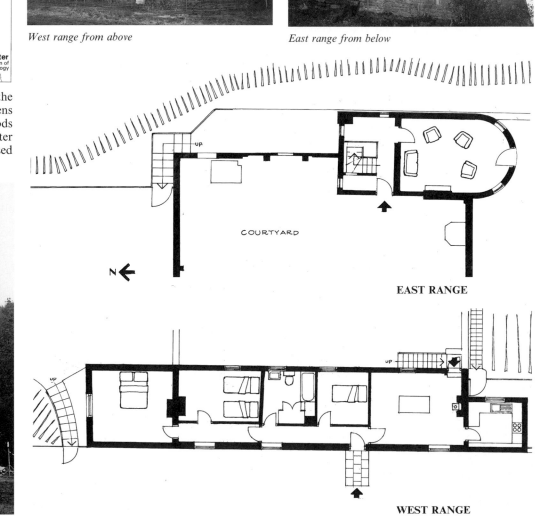

East range from below

COURTYARD

N

EAST RANGE

WEST RANGE

Langley Gatehouse, Acton Burnell, Shropshire

Like all the best buildings this one is hard to find. To add confusion, its two faces are each quite different: one, formerly presented to the outside word but now looking onto a farmyard, is of plain, dressed stone. The other, which once looked inwards at Langley Hall (demolished by 1880) is timber-framed, in the best local tradition. Both are Jacobean, although the lower part of the outer wall was already ancient when Sir Humphrey Lee added this great gatehouse above it about 1610.

The new building was probably for the Steward, or important guests. The parlour, over the gate passage, was panelled (and is again) with a moulded plaster cornice. On either side are rooms of generous size, and above are attics, squeezed in among the aisled structure of the queen-post roof. The roof itself is covered with moss-covered Harnage stone slates, thick with fossilised shells.

The gatehouse was near to collapse when, as a joint operation with English Heritage, we began work on it in 1992—its north east corner post, indeed, appeared to be supported solely

by a wine bottle wedged beneath its decayed foot. The exemplary quality of the repairs, by Treasures of Ludlow, is a pleasure to see; as also is the view from the main windows down a wide valley to the Wrekin.

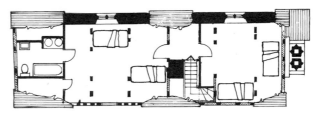

SECOND FLOOR

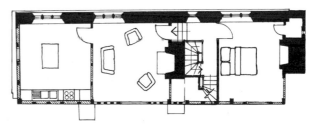

FIRST FLOOR

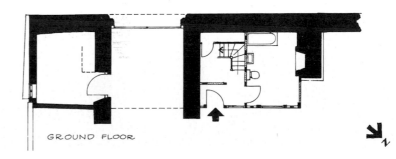

GROUND FLOOR

Laughton Place, Nr. Lewes, Sussex

This building has an illustrious pedigree, which it wears with the lonely and battered dignity of a nobleman fallen on hard times. It was once the chief manor of the Pelham family, without whom eastern Sussex would not have been as it is; and was rebuilt in 1534 on a grand scale, round a courtyard and with terracotta decoration in the newest Renaissance fashion. But by 1600 they had abandoned it, driven by the damp to build again on higher ground. Slowly it decayed until there was little left beyond this bold outlook tower.

Then about 1750, Henry Pelham, politician and brother to the splendid Duke of Newcastle, had the idea of surrounding the tower with a Gothick farmhouse. The result was very charming, with a pediment between crenellated side-wings, and pointed windows. Thus it continued until sold by the Pelhams in 1927. The new owner pulled down the wings, leaving once again only the outlook tower, forlorn in the Marshes, within the wide circle of the Downs.

When we bought it in 1978, the tower had great cracks in its sides, and the floors had fallen in—much engineering went into its repair. The rooms inside are plain, apart from

the delicate arabesque decoration of the terracotta windows, and moulded terracotta doors; and, wherever possible, the Pelham Buckle, the badge won by prowess in the Middle Ages and used as a family emblem ever since, which shows that the building, if long neglected, was once something to be proud of.

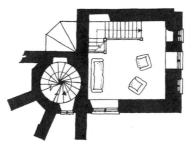
FIRST FLOOR

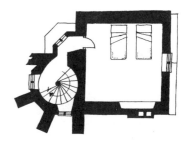
THIRD FLOOR

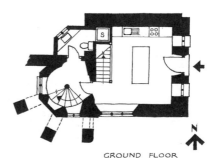
GROUND FLOOR

SECOND FLOOR

Lettaford, North Bovey, Devon

The fringes of Dartmoor gave a surprisingly good living to those who had the tenacity to carry on in its sometimes harsh climate, grazing their cattle on the rough upland pasture, cultivating crops as they could in the tiny fields lower down. There they were throughout the Middle Ages, with their own way of life and their own economy, carefully adapted to suit their surroundings and best seen now in the long-houses in which they chose to live, found nowhere else in such numbers in the comfortable South of England. It is in the building of these on a grander scale, with fine masonry and even carved ornament, that we see evidence of renewed activity from 1500 on, when a growth of population and prosperity in Devon as a whole led to new buildings and new settlements.

Lettaford is an old settlement, men having lived here from before 1300. The public road that leads to it breaks up into tracks, taking you onto the moor itself; and all its three farmhouses are, in origin at least, sixteenth century long-houses. It is sited in a hollow for shelter, its buildings grouped around a green, with a former Methodist chapel the only one not related directly to farming. It is like many other,

similar, hamlets but few remain so secret or complete. The self-contained, resourceful life of an upland people goes on around you as it always has; and the world contracts to Dartmoor's limits, beyond which only the adventurous go.

Higher Lettaford

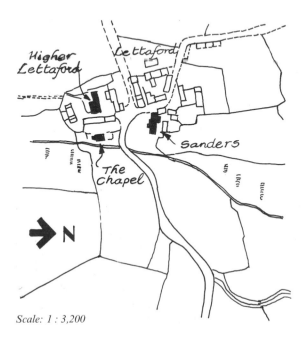

Scale: 1 : 3,200

61

Lettaford

Higher Lettaford had been empty for some years when we bought it in 1987. It was once a long-house, but about 1840 its lower end was re-built, most comfortably, by two Misses Pynsent, who may have run a small Nonconformist school here. Their house has large windows, and a verandah, introducing a whiff of Torquay and a life of ease to this hard-working place.

The Chapel is a plain granite building typical of rural Nonconformity, built by Miss Pynsent of Higher Lettaford in 1866. Firstly Bible Christian, and later Methodist, it closed in 1978. With little chance of survival, its loss would have been a pity for Lettaford, so we took it on. Here two of you can cook, eat and sleep all in one big room, with an open fire, tucked away at the side of the green beside a small stream.

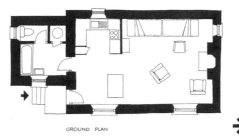

GROUND PLAN

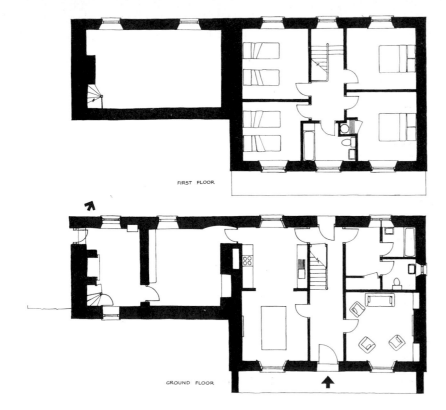

FIRST FLOOR

GROUND FLOOR

62

Sanders is a near perfect Dartmoor long-house of about 1500, arranged on the usual plan of inner room, hall, cross-passage and shippon, all under one roof, with a shouldered porch originally the entrance for both cows and people. The walls are made of blocks of granite ashlar, some of them enormous. This was a house of high quality, but it declined into a labourer's cottage long enough ago to avoid damaging improvements of any kind.

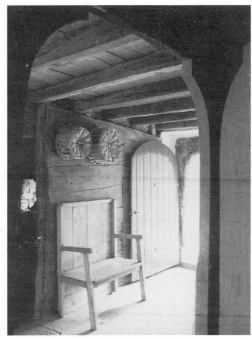

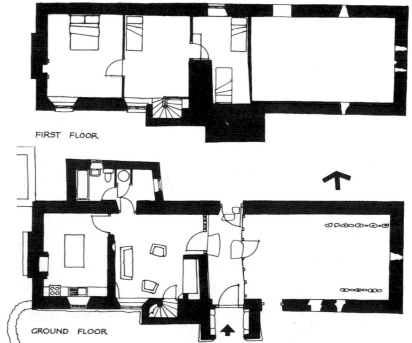

FIRST FLOOR

GROUND FLOOR

The Library, Stevenstone, Nr. Great Torrington, Devon

The Library, and its smaller companion the Orangery, stand in well-mannered incongruity beside the ruins of Victorian Stevenstone, with the remains of a grand arboretum around them. Stevenstone was rebuilt by the very last of the Rolles in 1870, but these two pavilions survive from an earlier remodelling of 1710–20. The façade of the Library, with its giant order and modillion cornice, looks like the work of a lively, probably local, mason-architect, familiar with the work of such as Talman and Wren.

Why a library in the garden? Probably it started life as a perfectly ordinary banqueting house, and only assumed its more learned character later on. Why it should have done so is a mystery, of a pleasantly unimportant kind. By the time we first saw it, when it came up for sale in 1978, the bookshelves had been dispersed, and the Library had been a house for many years, the fine upper room divided and the loggia closed in, while the Orangery was about to collapse altogether. We put new roofs on both buildings and, on the Library, a new eaves cornice carved from 170 feet of yellow pine by a

local craftsman, Robert Barnett. The loggia is open again, and the main room has returned to its full size. To stay in this particularly handsome building, even without the books, is an enlightening experience.

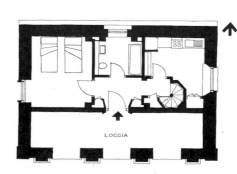

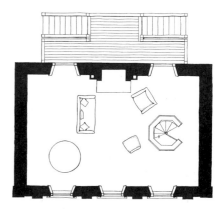

GROUND FLOOR   LOGGIA   FIRST FLOOR

There are two beds in the Orangery, 200 ft from the main building. It is unheated and therefore not recommended for winter use

Lock Cottage, Stoke Pound, Worcestershire

For up to 4 people

We hope that this lock cottage will give you a taste for travel by canal, which is the prime way to see England at walking pace without actually having to walk. Until the 1950s many such handsome, unpretentious buildings served and graced our canal system; but they were demolished ruthlessly. Indeed it was, in particular, the destruction of Thomas Telford's Junction House at Hurlestone on the Shropshire Union canal which maddened us into starting the Landmark Trust.

This survivor lies on the Worcester & Birmingham canal, built between 1790 and 1815, which runs for thirty miles from Diglis Basin in Worcester to Gas Street in Birmingham. Birmingham, as boaters all discover, is on a hill, and it takes fifty-eight locks in sixteen miles to lift this canal from the Severn to the Birmingham level. Of these locks, thirty are here at Tardebigge, the longest flight in Britain.

Our cottage is between locks 31 and 32, by bridge 49, a bridge as beautiful as all the others; canals are a wonderful demonstration that beauty and utility can be combined. Alas today in front of your windows will pass only pleasure

boats, but if you hang about at the lock, quite soon you will be offered a lift up the flight; and at the top, with its surprising view, you will, if you possess any spirit at all, decide to navigate one day still further, through the tunnel under the green hill beyond.

Before repair

FIRST FLOOR

GROUND FLOOR

65

Lower Porthmeor, Zennor, Cornwall

These houses are not of great age, but they represent a tradition as old as the tiny stone-hedged fields in which they stand, which have scarcely changed since the Iron Age. Lower Porthmeor is a Township, or farm hamlet, typical of this area where sometimes as many as four houses are grouped round a single farmyard. With their pleasant, sturdy granite buildings, such settlements can be seen dotted all along this wild north coast of west Penwith.

One of the houses here we have made into a home for the National Trust warden; another, **The Farmhouse**, is where you will stay, and is the finest of them. It was built soon after 1800 and has a handsome front of granite ashlar, paid for perhaps with money from the tin stamps nearby. Upstairs are further hints of wealth, in a bedroom with a dado and a pretty fireplace. But the great chimneypiece in the kitchen has a granite monolith for the lintel, common to many older houses in the area.

We bought the farm, which had been derelict for some years, in conjunction with the National Trust, which is seeking to preserve as much as possible of the landscape and life of Penwith. It is indeed a landscape to treasure,

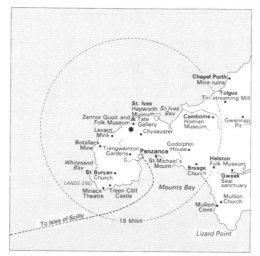

with its ridge of high moorland, and in contrast the green coastal shelf of farmland, suspended above the Atlantic. Little valleys run down to sandy coves (Porthmeor means great cove), between dramatic headlands, while the wild flowers are in such profusion as to be almost intoxicating.

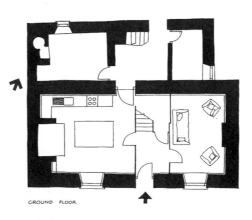

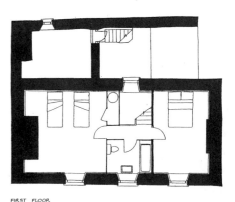

GROUND FLOOR

FIRST FLOOR

Arra Venton, a house of somewhat mixed parentage, came on the market just after we had taken on Lower Porthmeor. There were once two buildings here, a chapel and a smithy, onto one end of which a cottage was added early this century. Then, in 1952, the whole was joined together, in an eccentric if imaginative fashion. Its curiosities included a window made of a single sheet of glass moulded into a bow. Altered again since then, and treated and painted in an unsympathetic way, it spoiled the elemental landscape of which it is part, and looked horrible from our other buildings. So we bought it, and de-improved it, to make it simple and unified again; and very pleasant it is.

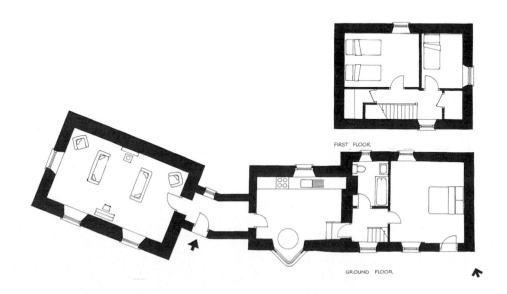

FIRST FLOOR

GROUND FLOOR

Lundy, Bristol Channel, Devon

The island of Lundy, in the approaches to the Bristol Channel, is three miles long and rises over four hundred feet out of the sea, commanding a tremendous view of England, Wales and the Atlantic. It has tall cliffs towards the south and west, with grass and heather on top, and steep sidelands with trees, shrubs and bracken in small hanging valleys on the east coast facing the mainland. There are three lighthouses (two in use), a castle, a church, an active farm, several handsome houses and cottages, a population of about fifteen, and no cars. Most of the buildings and all the field walls are made of the island's beautiful light-coloured granite.

When Lundy was taken on by the National Trust in 1969 (thanks mainly to the generosity of Sir Jack Hayward), we undertook to restore and run the island. The formidable task of tidying up and restoring the buildings and services for both visitors and residents took us over twenty years. Much of this work remains

invisible, but without it, ordinary people would soon have been unable to live on or visit the island.

The Tavern

Lundy offers the public a very rare experience. It is large enough to have a genuine life of its own which visitors can share and enjoy, but small and far enough away to be a world apart and undefaced. It offers both the pleasures of escape and the pleasures of participation— walks or wanderings high up, in the silence, looking east across the blue floor of the sea to the coast of Devon, or westward over the limitless Atlantic; or sociable visits to the tavern and shop. Opportunities abound for Field Studies of all kinds; and for the energetic there is rockclimbing, or diving and snorkelling in the Marine Nature Reserve. Everybody has the free run of the whole island, and it is surprising how much out of the ordinary there is to do and see at all times of the year.

Our handsome supply ship, the MS *Oldenburg*, runs throughout the year from Bideford or Ilfracombe, carrying day and staying visitors. On the island we have made it possible to stay at various levels of price and comfort—in cottages, in a hostel, or by camping—so that almost anyone can afford to be here.

Your arrival on the island is an event and the operation of getting you ashore, by launch, to land under a beetling cliff as all your predecessors have since time began, has been carefully perfected. To come here, even for the day, is a small adventure. But all those who experience the space and light, the life of the island, and the natural beauty on every hand, have thereafter something in common which they treasure.

If you would like to know more, we can send you, free, our full colour guide to staying on Lundy.

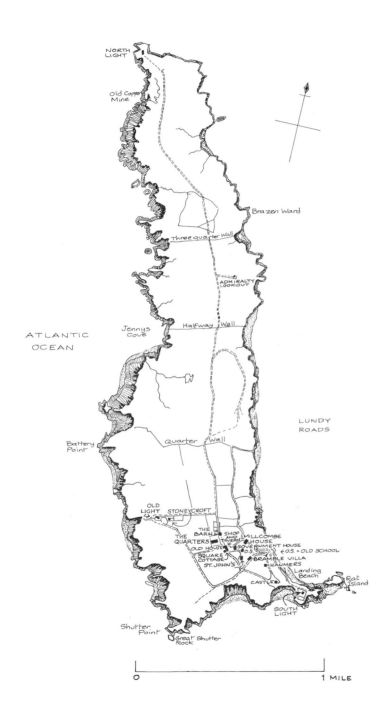

Lundy

The Castle was built by Henry III about 1250, and paid for by the sale of rabbits. High up on the south-east point of the island, it replaced the earlier castle of the unruly Mariscos, which stood in Bull's Paradise behind the farm. In the Civil War Lundy was held for the Royalists to the very end by Thomas Bushell, who rebuilt the castle. He owned a silver mine and tradition says he minted coins here. By 1787 cottages had been built round the small courtyard inside the Keep. These have decayed and been rebuilt several times, most recently by us. They are snug and sociable, inward-looking except for one or two windows in the outer walls which have spectacular marine views.

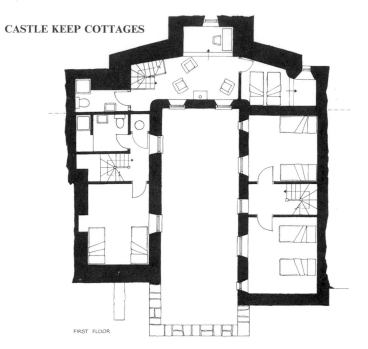

CASTLE KEEP COTTAGES

Castle Keep North, South and East

FIRST FLOOR

Castle Cottage is on the left

Castle Cottage, built onto the outside of the Keep, is the old post office and cable station, with an addition made by the Harman family. It does not improve the look of the castle, but it makes such a good place to spend a holiday, with a wonderful view, that we have not had the heart to demolish it.

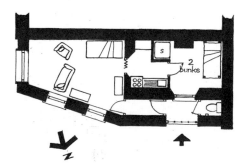

CASTLE KEEP EAST

CASTLE KEEP NORTH

CASTLE KEEP SOUTH

GROUND FLOOR

Millcombe House was built in 1836 for the Heaven family, looking down a wooded valley and out to sea. Most of the furniture in its well-proportioned rooms is also nineteenth century, and some of the pictures are very interesting. The curious inward-sloping roof, which we have restored to its original form, was designed to catch rainwater.

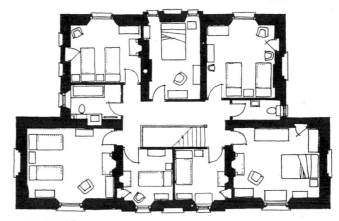

FIRST FLOOR

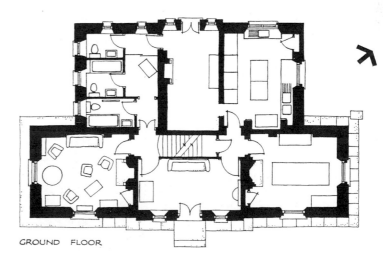

GROUND FLOOR

71

Lundy

The Old Light, completed in 1820, was designed by Daniel Asher Alexander. Built of Cyclopean blocks of granite, it stands on the highest point of the island. The keeper's quarters are still divided into the two original flats, very satisfying in design and detail. The upper flat is the only dwelling on Lundy to look out over the northern part of the island.

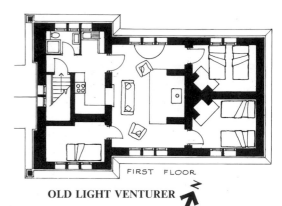

OLD LIGHT VENTURER

FIRST FLOOR

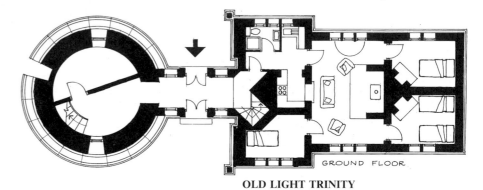

GROUND FLOOR

OLD LIGHT TRINITY

Big and Little St John's are a pair of single storey cottages, added by the Harman family to an existing granite barn in the St John's valley.

They are not very handsome but they occupy a fine position, sheltered and secluded, with a beautiful view towards Devon.

Stoneycroft is on the right

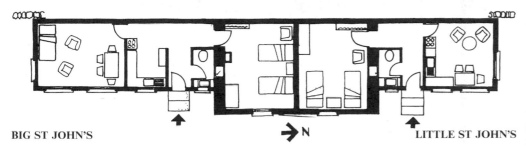

BIG ST JOHN'S

→N

LITTLE ST JOHN'S

Stoneycroft was where the lighthouse inspectors stayed when they visited Lundy. It stands in its own walled enclosure, near the Old Light, facing south.

The Old School, long known as 'the Blue Bung', lies near the St John's Cottages and shares much the same outlook. It is a small building of corrugated iron, with a snug interior lined with matchboarding. Designed and made with care, in better times, it has, like many such buildings, considerable point and charm.

→N

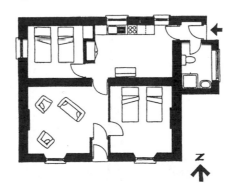

Stoneycroft

Old Light Cottage was the lighthouse keepers' store, solidly built of granite to the usual Trinity House standard. We have equipped it, and the Radio Room near the Tavern, for those who come to Lundy on their own. It stands in the same compound as the Old Light, and has in it just about everything that one person can want.

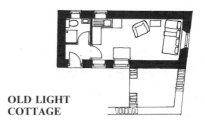

OLD LIGHT COTTAGE

Lundy

The Old House is the most handsome building on the island, in perhaps the best position, and made of the best-looking granite. Built in the late eighteenth century, it had been sadly altered: we removed large additions from three sides, and divided it, invisibly, into two.

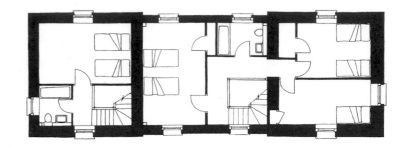

FIRST FLOOR

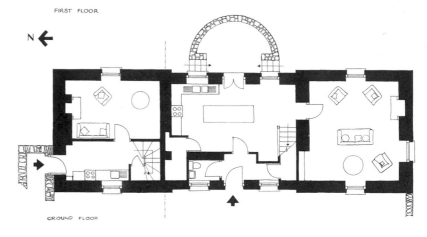

N ←

GROUND FLOOR

OLD HOUSE NORTH   **OLD HOUSE SOUTH**

The Radio Room is a small, solid building in the walled garden behind the Old House, which used to house the ancient wireless transmitter with which for many years the island kept in touch with the mainland. It is cosy and self-contained, with an east-facing terrace.

THE RADIO ROOM

Square Cottage was formed by us from the remains of the nineteenth century quarry manager's house. Its front door opens onto the garden behind the Old House, but to south and east it has spectacular views, especially from the upstairs sitting room, which has a good Victorian fireplace. It also has central heating, using up surplus energy from the island's generator, and so, with the Old House, is very comfortable in winter.

Government House was designed by Philip Jebb to house whoever runs the island, and to make use of and preserve the fine granite dressings left when additions to the Old House were removed. However, our present agent and his wife unselfishly preferred to remain where they were already, and so it is available for you to stay in. It is one of the best houses we possess, and so well sited that it seems always to have been there, sheltered on three sides and looking down the Millcombe valley towards the sea.

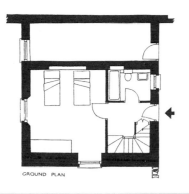

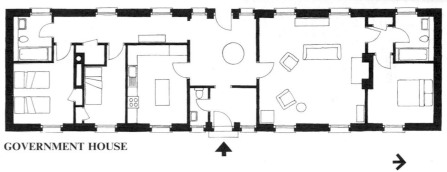

GROUND PLAN

FIRST FLOOR

GOVERNMENT HOUSE

Square Cottage on the left, with The Old House to its right

Lundy

The Barn, which was roofless when we arrived, is now a comfortable hostel, at the centre of island life. The rooms are lined with varnished wood; it has a large living room with a big open fire and, from the sleeping gallery, one of the best views on the island.

The Quarters (not illustrated) are two long wooden buildings, one behind the other, put up originally to house teams of builders on the island. They offer a party more comfort and privacy than the Barn. The big living room has a fine outlook towards Hartland Point.

Admiralty Lookout (formerly Tibbetts), built to a functional and most satisfying design, was put up as an Admiralty lookout in 1909, on the second highest part of the island. It is about 1¾ miles along the main track to the North and is as remote and simple as anyone could wish. It is said that from it fourteen lighthouses can be seen on a clear night. The interior is lined with varnished matchboarding and keeps its original purposeful atmosphere.

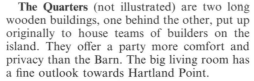
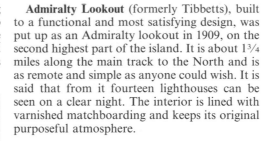

The Barn

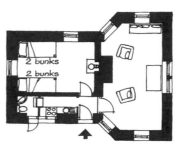

ADMIRALTY LOOKOUT

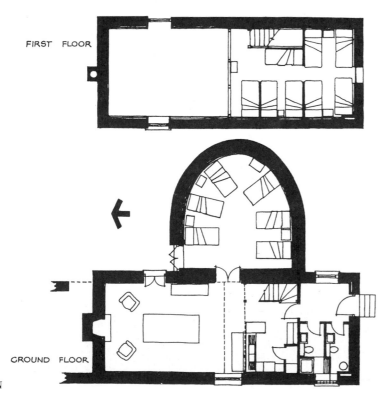

FIRST FLOOR

GROUND FLOOR

THE BARN

76

Bramble Villa, West and **East**, is in the St John's Valley, on the site of a ruinous corrugated iron building of the same name, and the same rather colonial appearance. It was shipped, ready made, from the mainland, and put up to house those who were to carry out the restoration work for us on Lundy. **East** looks over the sea towards Devon and has the light off the sea in its rooms. **West** also has a glimpse of the sea, but is more sheltered.

Hanmers was built by a fisherman in 1902. He chose a good site, a dip in the hill, on the path from the beach to the castle, so the place is sheltered but has the usual wonderful view out to sea towards Devon. It is weatherboarded outside and its interior is also of wood, painted white in the front rooms, which gives it a warm and solid feel.

Bramble Villa West

Bramble Villa East

Hanmers

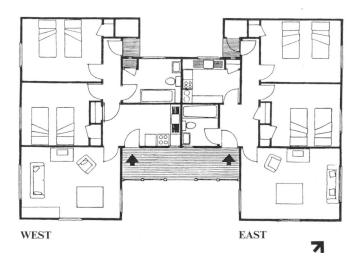

WEST   **EAST**

Luttrell's Tower, Eaglehurst, Southampton

This is an exceptionally fine Georgian folly, possibly the only surviving work of Thomas Sandby, first Professor of Architecture at the Royal Academy. It stands on the shore of the Solent looking towards Cowes. The view, particularly of ships entering and leaving Southampton by the deep water channel, is magnificent—as, in another way, is the sight to landward, from its top, of the Fawley refinery and power station. It also has the magic of those places where trees, especially yews and ilexes as here, come right down to the salt sea's edge.

It was built for Temple Luttrell, a Member of Parliament (but reputedly a smuggler here) who died in Paris in 1803, during the French Revolution. His brother-in-law, Lord Cavan, who commanded our forces in Egypt from 1801, was the next owner and brought home with him the two mysterious feet on a plinth of Nubian granite, now at the tower and thought to be the base of a XIXth dynasty statue of Rameses II.

Thereafter the tower passed through various hands; Queen Victoria nearly bought it (with Eaglehurst House) instead of Osborne, and

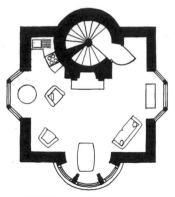

Marconi used it for his wireless experiments of 1912. Sir Clough Williams-Ellis designed the monumental gates and double staircase which give access to it from the beach, too grand really for anyone but Neptune.

We bought the tower in 1968. Inside, all the rooms have fine chimney pieces, and the top room, which we have arranged so that you can cook, eat and sit in this splendid eyrie, has fine plaster and shellwork as well. There is a tunnel from the basement to the beach, perhaps made for the smuggling Member.

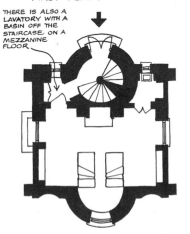

SECOND FLOOR

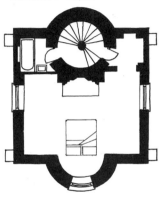

FIRST FLOOR

THERE IS ALSO A LAVATORY WITH A BASIN OFF THE STAIRCASE ON A MEZZANINE FLOOR

GROUND FLOOR

Lynch Lodge, Alwalton, Nr. Peterborough

Alwalton lies in the extreme north of the county of Huntingdon, on the river Nene a few hundred yards from the Great North Road. Despite its nearness to poor overgrown Peterborough it has a quiet, open village street, a cul de sac ending in a patch of green, on which stands the Lynch Lodge. This building is the fine, two-storey Jacobean porch from the Dryden's house at Chesterton, where the poet often stayed with his favourite cousin. It was brought here when the house was demolished in 1807, and erected as a lodge to Milton Park by the Fitzwilliam family, who had a dower-house in the village. The Lynch drive having been closed (not surprisingly as it was ten miles long), it now presides over a farm entrance and a rough track to the river.

We were told about it by a neighbour and bought it from the Fitzwilliam estate. Never a very convenient dwelling, it had been altered and enlarged over the years to accommodate bigger families. We have restored it to its original form, with one room up and one room down, joined by a new staircase.

From the logbook

"Carol singers from the church appeared at the Lodge on our first evening".

"The highlight of my week was seeing a kingfisher for the first time flying low across the river".

"Were visited by the local police who didn't want to leave until they got a guided tour".

"On with the jigsaw!"

"Peterborough Cathedral—massive, impressive, free from clutter inside".

"It is surprising how much a family can have to say to one another without prompting or filling-in from the outside world".

"Every time we come indoors the smell of wood-smoke (and hot cross buns) makes my nose feel very pleased for the rest of myself".

GROUND FLOOR

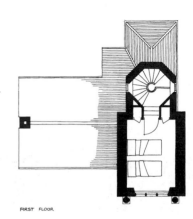

FIRST FLOOR

The Mackintosh Building, Comrie, Perthshire

This building was designed by Charles Rennie Mackintosh and dates from 1903–4, a time when he was doing his best work (see p. 52). It was commissioned by a local draper and ironmonger, Peter Macpherson and had long been overlooked; but there it is, a shop with a flat above, and workrooms in the attics, all just as it was when built. The flat passed into separate ownership some years ago, but we were able to reunite the two, by buying the flat in 1985, and then the shop as well, from Mr. Macpherson's granddaughter. In it you can still buy drapery, along with most other things.

We have redecorated the flat, which has good and characteristic detail. The main room runs into the projecting turret, or *tourelle*, which Mackintosh added to the outer angle of the building in a nod towards Scottish Baronial architecture. This gives it an airy feel, and a pleasant view of the River Earn and the wooded hills beyond.

Comrie is an unfussy highland town, with a bridge over a pebbly river, a whitewashed

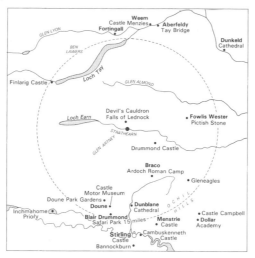

church and a small square, on the corner of which, right at the centre of things, stands this building.

From the logbook

"Magnificent countryside and enough to do and see to fill a lifetime."

"It has made us quite determined to find out more about Charles Rennie Mackintosh."

"We were especially fond of the bay window—looking out on to the world of Comrie."

"The marriage of Mackintosh building to Landmark Trust is a truly happy one."

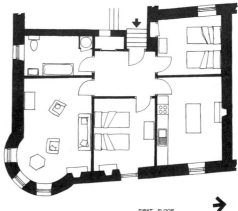

FIRST FLOOR

Maesyronen Chapel, Glasbury-on-Wye, Powys

We have here the neat and tiny cottage built before 1750 onto the end of one of Wales's shrines of Nonconformity, the Maesyronen chapel. The chapel itself, converted from a barn in 1696, dates from the early, vernacular, days when any suitable building was made use of for enthusiastic worship. Although officially founded just after the Act of Toleration, it had probably been used for secret meetings before that, which explains its isolated position. Its simple layout and furniture, added as and when the congregation could afford it, is of the basic pattern which prevailed for the next two centuries. It has high box pews and a higher pulpit on the long wall, lit from behind by a window, and all of a plainness which fully conveys the essentials of this new and radical rural faith.

The chapel, where services are still held, is cared for by Trustees, who asked for our help. By taking a lease on the cottage, we hope we have given both buildings a future. Staying here, perched on a high shelf above the Wye, with views to the Black Mountains, you can sample a different and earlier kind of life to that which grew up around the chapels of the South Wales valleys in the nineteenth century, which has tended to eclipse what went before it in the public imagination.

From the logbook

"Opened our Christmas stockings to the atmospheric sounds of Christmas carols filtering through the wall from the chapel."

"Our dog had the best holiday a dog could have."

"We never tired at gazing at the view."

"The bookshelf is full of treasures."

"The common is great for kite flying."

"We saw herons and a kingfisher at Glasbury near the bridge."

"We will miss the mountains tomorrow night."

The cottage is on the left

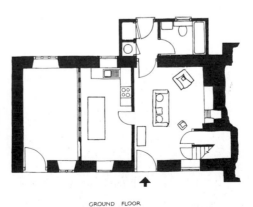

GROUND FLOOR

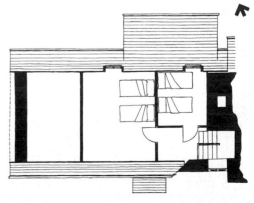

FIRST FLOOR

81

Manor Farm, Pulham Market, Nr. Diss, Norfolk

Manor Farm is a vernacular building, put up by men who had done the same job many times before, and knew just what they were doing. It is late Elizabethan—South Norfolk was then more thickly wooded and populated than today—and apart from minor additions, has not been altered since. It was the home of a yeoman farmer, who added to his income with a bit of weaving: Pulham work, a furnishing fabric, was well-known. To judge by his house, he was quite comfortably off.

In the first half of this century a good living was more difficult to come by for a small farmer. Manor Farm decayed, and its vulnerable thatch and plaster disintegrated. The oak panelling and moulded beams were nearly sold as antiques. But in 1948 it was recognised for what it was, and rescued in the nick of time by Mr. and Mrs. Dance of the SPAB, who repaired it to the highest of William Morris's standards.

Thirty years later, if it was to go on as a permanent home, it would have needed a good deal of modernisation, which would not inevitably have been in its best interests. So in 1979 we took it on. Such improvements as were needed we contained within an eighteenth century addition, leaving the yeoman's house in all its rich simplicity.

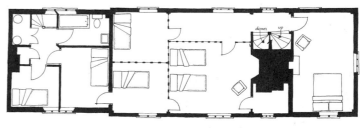

FIRST FLOOR

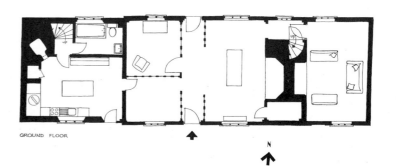

GROUND FLOOR

Margells, Branscombe, Devon

From outside this is just a plain stone cottage, pleasant enough if unremarkable; but inside it is another matter. The broad passage running across the middle of the house has oak partitions on each side, and both the downstairs rooms have heavily moulded oak ceilings. Upstairs the rooms are all open to the roof, and in one of them is a wall painting. The staircase has solid oak treads and all the doorways are of well above average quality. It is a very strong, interesting and well preserved interior, dating from the end of the sixteenth century.

What is all this doing in so small a house? The explanation may be that this was the parlour wing of a larger house which was later divided into several cottages. Whatever the answer, the result is most satisfying.

Moreover the surroundings are extremely pleasant. Margells is one of a group of old cottages, which includes a distinctly agreeable pub. Near the house a stream of water comes out of a spout in the wall and flows away under the road. Opposite, over the roofs, a wood climbs up a hill, and beyond that is the sea.

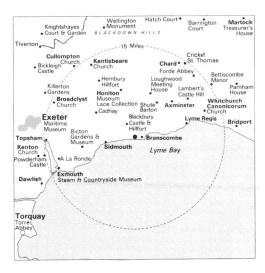

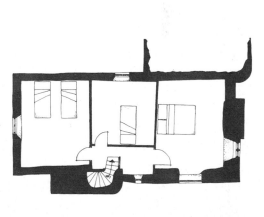

GROUND FLOOR

FIRST FLOOR

83

Marshal Wade's House, Abbey Churchyard, Bath

This is no vernacular affair, as so many of our places are, but a sophisticated building of about 1720 in the very centre of the town. Once there were others like it, but they have gone, taking with them the reputation of good architects practising in Bath before the Woods. They must have found a good patron in George Wade (made Field Marshal in 1744) who was the town's M.P. and whose London house was designed by Lord Burlington.

When we took it on in 1975, we restored the windows and the shop front, and decluttered and restored the interiors. Later, we cleaned the front too, with sprinkled water and lime poultices to dissolve encrusted grime.

The second floor rooms have good panelling, and all the windows look along the west front of the Abbey. From here, on a level with the angels, you can see the great carving of Jacob's ladder. There is also an exceptional view from the bathroom, and from the bath.

All around there are more good things to see

within walking distance than almost anywhere in Britain. Leave your car behind; come by train, live over the shop, just be in Bath.

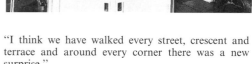

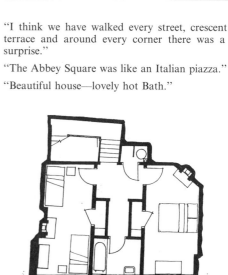

From the logbook

"The nearest to Florence you get in England, with stunning views all the way to trees on the hills."

"We've enjoyed staying with Marshal Wade."

"The Abbey is breathtaking."

"This sophisticated abode a splendid start to a week filled with architectural delights."

"I think we have walked every street, crescent and terrace and around every corner there was a new surprise."

"The Abbey Square was like an Italian piazza."

"Beautiful house—lovely hot Bath."

SECOND FLOOR   THIRD FLOOR

The Martello Tower, Aldeburgh, Suffolk

This is the largest and most northerly of the chain of towers put up by the Board of Ordnance to keep out Napoleon. Built in the shape of a quatrefoil for four heavy guns, nearly a million bricks were used in its construction. It stands at the root of the Orford Ness peninsular, between the River Alde and the sea, a few hundred yards from Aldeburgh. We bought it, sadly damaged, in 1971, with eight acres of saltings.

We removed the derelict 1930s superstructure (by Justin Vulliamy, once rather elegant), repaired the outer brickwork and parapet (a tremendous job) and restored the vaulted interior, which has a floor of teak, and an intriguing echo. Here you may live with the sea, the wind sometimes, the light at Orford Ness flashing at night, and Aldeburgh at just the right distance. The stone-flagged battery on the roof, with the mountings of guns and a high, thick parapet for shelter, is a very pleasant place to be. Amber and bloodstones, brought by glaciers from

From the logbook

"Most lasting memory: the sea".

"It's worth climbing the tower at Orford Castle and looking with proprietary eye at the Martello Tower on the horizon".

"November: fish stew on the roof for Sunday lunch".

"We watched an eclipse of the moon from the roof".

"Real solid furniture to go with the real solid tower".

"Games and talk happily replaced the goggle box".

"Rule Britannia has an especial feeling sung here".

Scandinavia, have been found on the beach. Many visitors bring sailing dinghies.

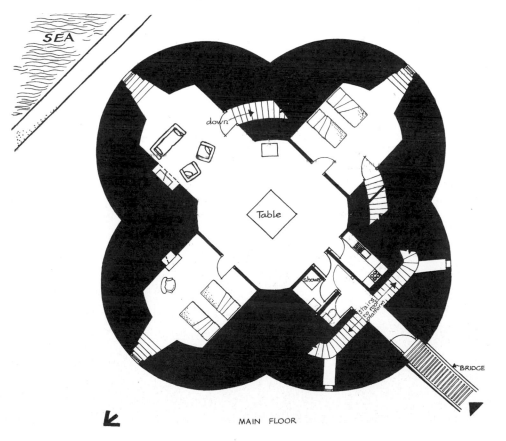

SEA

Table

down

Shower

STAIRS to roof platform

BRIDGE

MAIN FLOOR

Monkton Old Hall, Pembroke, Dyfed

Although much altered and rebuilt, the Old Hall has a strongly medieval character, a mixture of spareness and solidity. It dates from before 1400 and was probably the guest house of a small priory outside the walls of Pembroke. Just off the pilgrim route to St. David's, and close to a great castle, the monks could expect to put up any number of people at unexpected times. Since then the house has been left to become ruinous, and then been rescued, at least twice.

Its Victorian saviour was J. R. Cobb, a scholar and romantic who restored several castles in South Wales. In the 1930s it was discovered again, by Miss Muriel Thompson, another romantic. She repaired the house, with help from Clough Williams-Ellis, and created an exceptional garden, on a long terrace with a grandstand view of Pembroke Castle. She wanted to share her home with others, to revive a monastic sense of hospitality: many people came to stay and her Christmas parties were famous. It was the memory of this and the appeal the Old Hall has, especially for children,

that made Mrs Campbell, to whom it was left, think of passing it on to us. Whether you make your own pilgrimage to St. David's, or spend the day on the beach, the house will welcome you back, to warm yourself in the hall.

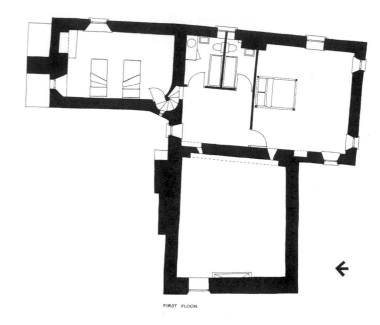

FIRST FLOOR

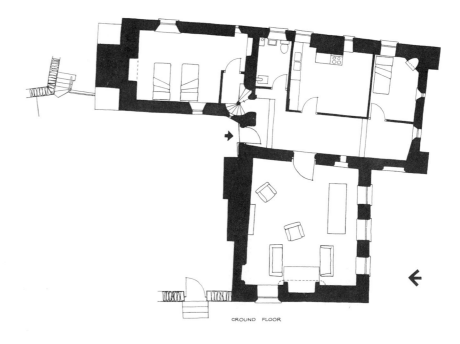

GROUND FLOOR

Morpeth Castle, Northumberland

The walls of a new castle in Morpeth were built soon after 1200, on a hill overlooking the River Wansbeck. Our gatehouse was added a century later, more for show than defence. Its builder, Lord Greystoke, wanted its presence felt, because this was to be a court-house, in which manorial justice was dispensed—an important function in the unruly Borders. The court was held on the first floor, in a large room divided by a screen. Behind this the plaintiffs waited but it now hides nothing more dangerous than the kitchen.

Between sittings the gatehouse served more domestic purposes, probably as a lodging for the bailiff. These arrangements disappeared in later alterations, however, once just before 1700 and again in 1860. Each time, a new house was formed within the walls, with new floors, partitions and stairs. We have tried to keep something of each, but to make sense of the medieval layout as well.

Morpeth saw little warfare in the Middle Ages, though Border raids were an occupational hazard. The one great military event in the castle's history was in 1644 when a garrison of 500 Lowland Scots held it for Parliament for twenty days against 2,700 Royalists.

The castle stands on a small plateau, above the town and with fine views of it, but completely removed from the bustle. Once inside the curtain wall, whose circuit is battered but still complete, you could be inside the most remote Border stronghold instead of the former guardian of Northumberland's very pleasant capital.

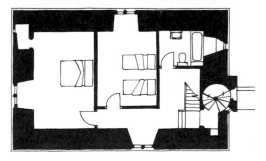

SECOND FLOOR

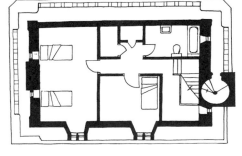

ATTIC FLOOR

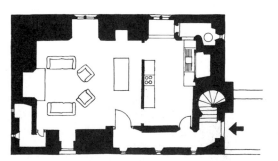

FIRST FLOOR

The Music Room, Sun Street, Lancaster

The Music Room had been well known for years as a building in distress, but nothing could be done because it had other buildings hard up against it on all four sides. On our first visit we had to reach it by walking through the toy warehouse of which it formed a part. We had to buy (a long job) all these buildings and demolish them to give the builders access.

It seems to have been built about 1730, as a garden pavilion, but its surroundings have long been overlaid with streets. In the nineteenth century the building became part of a stained glass factory. When we arrived it had a temporary roof, and many broken windows. Most of the plasterwork had fallen, but luckily almost all of it was in the building.

We turned the loggia into a shop by glazing the central Ionic arch and removing an inserted floor. It did not seem sensible to leave this large space lifeless and empty in the middle of a town. In front, with the City's help, we made a pedestrian square.

The plasterwork of the music room itself took 6000 hours of work to repair. It is an exceptional Baroque interior. On the walls are the muses: eloquence, history, music, astronomy, tragedy, rhetoric, dancing, comedy and amorous poetry; with Apollo over the fireplace. A fruitful goddess with a torch presides over the ceiling. One muse had vanished entirely and was re-created by the plasterers from Sutton Coldfield as a modern girl, big and busty, with a cheerful eye; she makes an excellent muse of dancing.

In the attic above, reached by a narrow stair, we made a flat. From it and from the small terrace on its roof there are distant views over Lancaster (including a fine view of the Castle from the sink); and at all times, waiting for you to enter it, there is the stillness of the music room below, both full and empty at the same time, as is the way with rich interiors.

Lancaster is a fine town, with many things worthy of attention—not least Rennie's monumental aqueduct on the Lancaster Canal, bridging the River Lune like a vestige of imperial Rome.

Before restoration

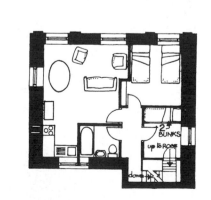

Naulakha, Brattleboro, Vermont, USA

In 1892, Rudyard Kipling and his new wife, Caroline, arrived in Vermont to stay with her family near Brattleboro. He was captivated by this new country, and resolved to settle there permanently. He bought eleven acres of gently sloping pasture, and over the next winter supervised the building of a house, which he called Naulakha, the jewel beyond price.

The plans for Naulakha were drawn by H. R. Marshall, but Kipling saw its design as very much his own. He called it a ship, with his study at the bow. Here he could write in closely-guarded privacy, with direct access to a verandah and flower garden. The main point of the house was the view, across woods and farmland to distant hills. Each room must enjoy this, making the house long and thin.

The Kiplings' ideal of a remote, creative life in Vermont did not prosper. They left Naulakha in 1896, and in 1902 they sold the house, with most of its furniture, which, carefully preserved by subsequent owners, we have now bought. Many of the rooms are still as Kipling knew them, including the study, in which he completed *The Jungle Books*.

Naulakha shows us a different Kipling to Bateman's in Sussex. Here he was unharnessed

by a romantic sense of history: each mark he made was his alone. And Vermont, with its forests and lakes, its quiet villages and unhurried life, summer music festivals and winter skiing, is fully as captivating as it was a century ago.

Kipling's study in 1991, with much of its original furniture

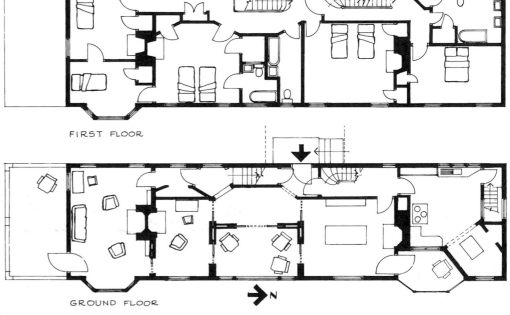

FIRST FLOOR

GROUND FLOOR

The Nicolle Tower, St. Clement's, Jersey

We were reluctant to take on this building until we actually went to see it. As often, there proved to be much more to it, and to the place, than a description or a snapshot could convey. Therefore we bought it, and its owner also sold us the field of 5 vergees in which the tower stands.

The field is called Le Clos de Hercanty. Hercanty means "tilted menhir", and one corner of the tower, tantalisingly, is built on a large half-buried slab of diorite. Moreover on this boulder is carved a compass rose and a date, 1644. So something has been going on here for a long time. It seems that the menhir was once a navigation mark, next to which a small rectangular lookout was built; to which in 1821 Philippe Nicolle, who had just bought the field, added a light-hearted Gothick octagon with the present very pretty sitting room on the first floor.

In 1943 the Germans, to make an observation or control position here, astutely raised the roof of the octagon by one more storey, so that from the air no change would be noticed. As this latest addition is part of the history of the

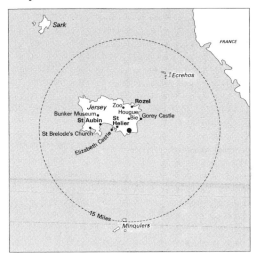

tower, we have left it there, with its slit eyes, and German ranging marks on its thick concrete ceiling. The tower stands 160 feet up, well back from the coast, with, it need hardly be said, views over the sea and island in every direction.

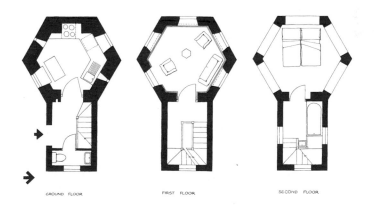

GROUND FLOOR   FIRST FLOOR   SECOND FLOOR

The New Inn, Peasenhall, Suffolk

The Local Authority sold us this row of ten cottages and a shop, then very dilapidated. The centre of the range is a late medieval hall-house, in use as an inn by 1478 and almost certainly built as such. Inns were then a fairly new invention, which had arrived in response to an increase in trade, and therefore of travellers. It was some time before they evolved into a distinct building type, however; until then most kept to the basic form that everyone knew, of a hall with chambers off it—and this is just what there is at the New Inn.

We repaired the hall (which is open to the public) and all the other cottages as well. The three oldest we kept as Landmarks. Two of them, at each end of the hall, are entered from it, as they would have been originally. The high end is the grander, with one particularly fine bedroom—a solar or great chamber with a crown-post roof.

At the backs of the cottages we removed some decayed sheds to make a yard and a place to hide cars. We also bought the land in front, closed the road which ran across it, and turned it into a village green.

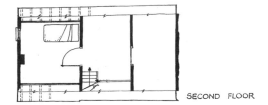

Peasenhall is a long, open village, with a stream running beside the road. It is much-visited by connoisseurs of sausages and ham, sold in more than one of its excellent shops.

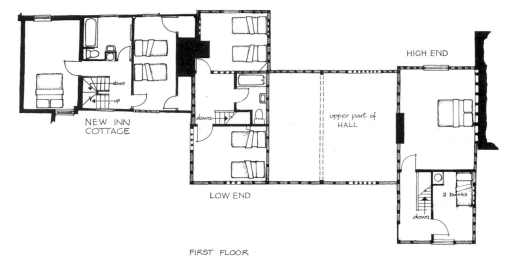

SECOND FLOOR

NEW INN COTTAGE

HIGH END

upper part of HALL

2 bunks

LOW END

FIRST FLOOR

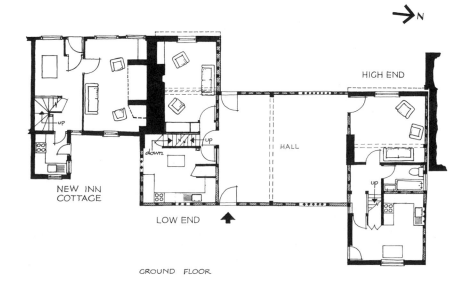

HIGH END

NEW INN COTTAGE

HALL

LOW END

GROUND FLOOR

92

10 North Street, Cromford, Derbyshire

North Street, a cul-de-sac named after the Prime Minister, was built in 1771 by Richard Arkwright to house his mill workers. It is the earliest planned industrial housing in the world, and the finest of its type ever built—vastly superior to that of the next century. The three-storey gritstone houses have one room on each floor, with a room for framework-knitting in the attic. Each has a small garden, and an allotment at a distance.

We bought six of the houses in 1974 from the Ancient Monuments Society, which had taken them on to save them from demolition. We then bought a further three houses, so that we now own most of one side of the street. We re-roofed and improved all nine, and restored the long windows of the attic workrooms. We kept the original interiors where they survived.

One house we repaired as a Landmark so that people can live in and appreciate this much inhabited street, and explore its remarkable surroundings. Here you will be what the traveller should be, in a tiny minority, an object of interest, not part of an unwanted herd. For those interested in industrial history, there is a

great deal to see—lead mines, the Cromford canal, the High Peak Railway, Arkwright's mills, and traces of the life they created. There is also Matlock Bath and Matlock, a very genuine old inland resort, at whose petrifying wells you can have your bowler hat turned into stone.

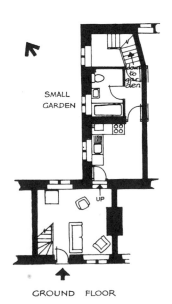

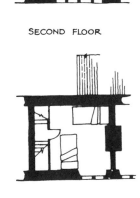

SMALL GARDEN

GROUND FLOOR

FIRST FLOOR

SECOND FLOOR

No. 10 is the second house on the right from this end

The Old Hall, Croscombe, Somerset

Originally the great hall of a manor house built by Sir William Palton about 1420, this building was for 250 years a Baptist chapel. It lies just north of the handsome parish church, and looks into a small, tranquil enclosure, part garden and part graveyard.

The Baptists, but for whom the building must have disappeared, made a number of harmless alterations. Removal of these, and the repair and consolidation of the tottering structure, with its wavy roof of pantiles like a shaken rug, revealed quite a grand hall with a fine arch-braced open roof.

In its south wall we found the great blocked arch of an oriel chamber, which once linked the hall to a vanished wing to the east. Beside it a rare medieval light bracket appeared, which has on it the arms of Sir William and his wife. The service end of the hall we turned into bedrooms and kitchen, simple rooms of wood and stone.

When working on this building, we were offered a fully-operational Gurney's Patent Stove from Romsey Abbey, which we installed here to give extra heat in the hall. Keeping it stoked up provides much entertainment, and some strenuous exercise.

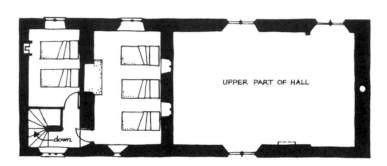

FIRST FLOOR

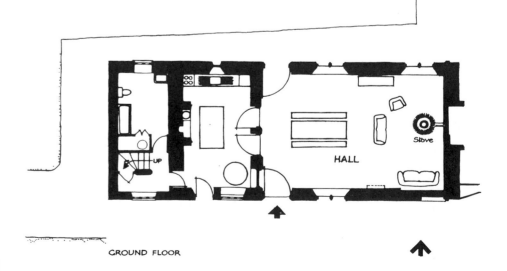

GROUND FLOOR

96

The Old Parsonage, Iffley, Oxford

Not only an important building in its own right, this house also conveys a strong impression of a parson's life in former days. A rectory was first built here at the same time as the elaborate Norman parish church a few yards away (and a rectory the earlier half of the house still is, modernised by us). Around 1500, a smart new wing was added, and in it are the handsome rooms which you will occupy. Some of them were later panelled, and given new fireplaces. In the parlour, probably added when J. C. Buckler worked on the house in 1857, is a tremendous Latin inscription running round all sides of the room—saying, in tall Gothic letters, "For we know that, if our earthly house were destroyed, we have a building of God, a house not made with hands, eternal in the heavens". Here, in this handsome, darkish room, you may sit looking down the garden, as did many a scholarly, leisured parson, pondering his sermon as he watched the Thames slide by.

The staircase, in a square tower of its own, is strong and plain, and reminiscent of staircases in Oxford colleges nearby. At the top is an attic bedroom from whose window there is a

romantic prospect of the spires and towers of Oxford. The house is entered straight off the pavement of Mill Lane, through the blank gable end, giving no hint of the long garden on the other side running down to the river at the tail of Iffley lock. The contrast is very agreeable.

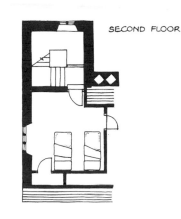

SECOND FLOOR

FIRST FLOOR

GROUND FLOOR

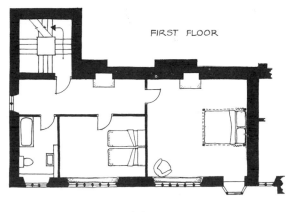

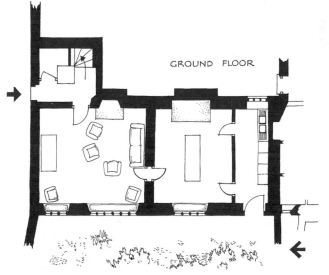

The Old Place of Monreith, Portwilliam, Wigtownshire

The Old Place, also known as Dowies, is a house that was left behind by the family that built it when they prospered, and went to live in a castle they bought nearby in 1683. It then became a farmhouse on their estate.

Before that, however, it was the home of the Maxwells, forebears of both Sir Herbert, historian and gardener, and the author Gavin Maxwell. Built around 1600, it is a typical, plain, lowland laird's house, still nominally fortified, with its farm steading around it.

When we bought it, it had been empty for twenty years. The roof and floors had fallen in, but two good fireplaces survived inside. We opened up the turnpike stair, which had been bricked up, and unblocked the main door with its stone panel for a coat of arms above.

The sea is only two miles away—the same coastline on which Gavin Maxwell grew up, at Elrig, seven miles away. Whithorn, across the peninsular, was a centre of the early Christian culture around the Irish Sea which produced such saints as Ninian, Patrick, and Columba. A cross once stood near the Old Place, but was moved in the last century and is now in

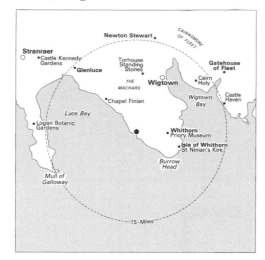

Whithorn museum. There remains behind a strong sense of a continuous civilised life, lived here over nearly two millenia, in a place that, even for a Landmark, is exceptionally quiet and remote.

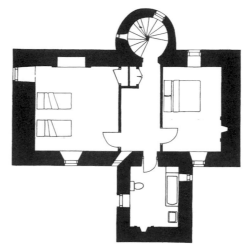

FIRST FLOOR

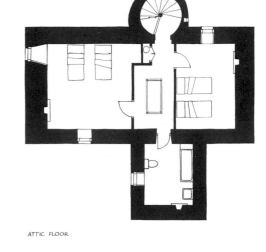

ATTIC FLOOR

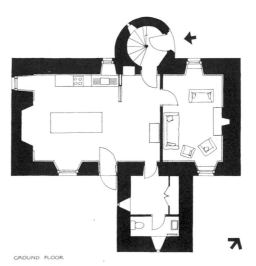

GROUND FLOOR

98

Peppercombe, Nr. Bideford, North Devon

The cliffs of the North Devon coast around Bideford Bay are broken by deep valleys which run almost down to the sea, but not quite. At the mouth there is usually a drop of some feet to the shore, down which tumbles a stream. Peppercombe is just such a valley, steep and wooded, and then opening out into a meadow, suspended forty foot or more above the beach. The stream goes straight down the final stretch in a fine waterfall but there is no need for you to do the same, because there is a gently sloping path as well. The cliffs themselves are particularly dramatic here, formed from an outcrop of red triassic stone. The whole magnificent coastline curves away in both directions, with Lundy on the horizon.

For centuries, the coombe belonged to the Portledge estate, and the Coffin family (latterly Pine-Coffins). In 1988, it was acquired by the National Trust, and we took on two of the buildings in it. **Bridge Cottage**, built about 1830, stands in woods at the top of the coombe. It had been empty for years, with a tarpaulin over its roof, but the walls of cob and stone were sound.

The kitchen and parlour have stone-flagged floors and good fireplaces, while the bedrooms follow the line of the roof, and seem slightly too small for furniture, as cottage bedrooms should.

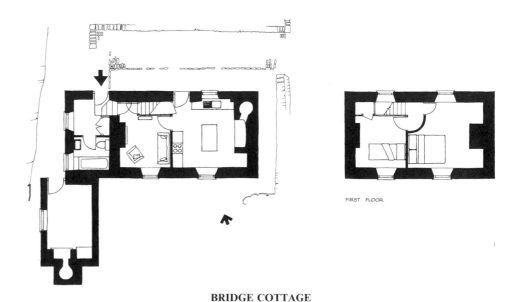

FIRST FLOOR

BRIDGE COTTAGE

At the mouth of the coombe is **Castle Bunga-low** which is just that, a 1920s Boulton and Paul bungalow. The company's archivist (it is still going strong in Norwich) found for us one catalogue of this period that survived the bomb-ing of the factory in 1940. It has tempting illustrations of 'Residences, Bungalows and Cottages', ranging from a substantial six-bedroom house on two storeys (at £4,000) to Bungalow B49, with just a bedroom, a living room and a verandah (in case you should live in the tropics). This, with brick foundations and carriage paid to the nearest Goods station, cost just £280.

Sadly, although a number of its brothers and sisters are there, our bungalow does not feature in the catalogue, but it is still just as tempting. Its weather-boarded walls are painted in railway colours, cream and brown (like the old GWR carriages), its windows are latticed and inside, the rooms are snug as only wood-lined rooms can be. Beside it are the remains of Pepper-combe Castle, a genuinely castellated seaside residence.

CASTLE BUNGALOW

Peters Tower, Lympstone, Devon

The Peters family were successful Liverpool merchants who in the nineteenth century took to serving their country as soldiers, sailors and landowners. William Peters who built this clock tower in 1885 as a memorial to his wife Mary Jane, was in the 7th Dragoons and lived in a biggish classical house nearby. His son was a General and his grandson an Admiral. On the latter's death in 1979 the Trustees of his estate offered us the tower as a gift.

It is no great work of architecture—a very distant and poor relation of St. Mark's in Venice—but it is part of the history of Lympstone, and it does stand, at the end of an alley, actually on the water's edge in this large and pleasant village, looking across the broad estuary of the Exe to the green fields beyond. Moreover, it is only a short walk from a railway station, so there is no need for those who stay here to have a car.

Accordingly we took it on, repaired the polychrome brick, restored the clock, and made the tower habitable again—it had been a refuge for fishermen stranded here by the weather. Every inch of space inside is valuable, so our architect, having spent some time at a boatyard, fitted it out with teak and brass and varnish. The views from all the windows are interesting and some spectacular, and there is a good deal of boating and sailing to be seen or participated in.

FIRST FLOOR

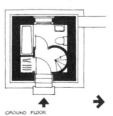

GROUND FLOOR

THIRD FLOOR

SECOND FLOOR

26 Piazza di Spagna, Rome

All architects, and many artists, owe a debt to Rome, and we had long wanted a foot-hold there. So when the Keats-Shelley Memorial Association launched an appeal for funds to maintain this building, we asked whether there was a part of it which we could occupy in return for helping them. Happily there was, a flat on the third floor, now restored by us to its condition in about 1800—spacious rooms with tiled floors and high, beamed ceilings painted in soft colours.

These are not the rooms in which Keats died in 1821—those are on the floor below—but they are identical in form and layout, and are more in a condition he would recognise. Every tall, shuttered window has a view unchanged almost since the days of the Grand Tour, and the sitting room looks up the Spanish Steps—certainly the world's grandest and most sophisticated outdoor staircase—to the church of S. Trinita dei Monti at the top. At the front door is Bernini's fountain in the form of a stone boat sinking into the Piazza di Spagna. There is

no motor traffic, but instead the noises of humanity; and if sometimes, to be fair, there is too much of that, especially at night, at least it is unusual—for example when the steps are cleared by water-cannon at midnight, or when the horse-drawn cabs, which form a rank at the far end of the Piazza, arrive over the cobbles, seemingly at dawn and at the gallop.

The Steps were designed in 1721 by Francesco de Sanctis, who also designed this house to fit in with his plan. It was probably apartments from the first, in a part of the city long frequented by foreign and particularly English visitors. There can be few places in Rome available now to their successors so central, so handsome, so famous or so unaltered as this.

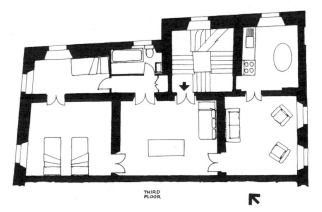

THIRD FLOOR

The Pigsty, Robin Hood's Bay, Yorkshire

Two pigs were the excuse for this exercise in primitive classicism, supposedly inspired by buildings seen by Squire Barry of Fyling Hall on his travels around the Mediterranean in the 1880s. By his use of timber columns, and his choice of inhabitants, he was perhaps trying to make a point about the roots of Classical architecture; or it may just have been that, as in the song, 'there was a lady loved a swine'. In Walter Crane's illustration for this song (from *The Baby's Opera*, published in 1877), the sty is given a Doric front, which might have been the starting point for Barry's eclectic inspiration.

The pigs' owners lived in a pair of neighbouring cottages, also architecturally embellished, but this time in more traditional Estate Gothic. It is several decades since they went in for pig-breeding, and alternative uses were hard to think of, until its owner heard of our activities, and then gave us a long lease. By the minimum of addition, and the insertion of glass here and there, we hope that we have made it acceptable to a higher breed of inhabitant; and although the living quarters will never be palatial, the view over Robin Hood's Bay from under the pediment is undoubtedly fit for an Empress.

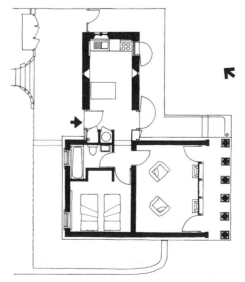

The Pineapple, Dunmore, Stirlingshire

The Pineapple is an elaborate summerhouse of two storeys, built for the 4th Earl of Dunmore. Though classical and orthodox at ground level, it grows slowly into something entirely vegetable; conventional architraves put out shoots and end as prickly leaves of stone. It is an eccentric work, of undoubted genius, built of the very finest masonry.

It probably began as a pavilion of one storey, dated 1761; and only grew its fruity dome after 1777, when Lord Dunmore returned, forcibly, from serving as Governor of Virginia. There, sailors would put a pineapple on the gatepost to announce their return home. Lord Dunmore, who was fond of a joke, announced his return more prominently.

The Pineapple presides over an immense walled garden. This, in the Scottish tradition, was built some distance from the house, to take advantage of a south-facing slope. To house the gardeners, stone bothies were built on either side of the Pineapple. These now make comfortable rooms for you to stay in, though you have to go out of doors to get from one part to the other.

The Pineapple and its surroundings are owned by the National Trust for Scotland; we

took a long lease of the whole in 1973 and restored all the buildings and the walled garden, which is now open to the public. At the back, where the ground level is higher, is a private garden for our visitors, with steps leading into the elegant room inside the Pineapple itself.

From the logbook

"The experience of actually living in such a building is so much more rewarding than merely visiting".

"We were very reluctant to leave the Pineapple".

"Farewell, old fruit".

"Dunmore Pottery has only an old kiln visible. Once famous for teapots".

"There is a hermit's cave nearby. It is hidden in a clump of rhododendron bushes and contains a chimney and a bed . . . We met a local gentleman exercising his greyhound who kindly showed us the route".

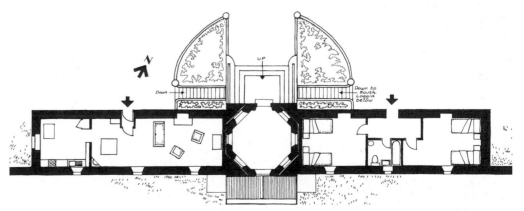

Plas Uchaf, Llangar, Nr. Corwen, Clwyd

This substantial hall-house was built about 1400, or perhaps before, on the side of a low hill in the Dee valley. Few houses of this age and type survive in Wales, and the quality of the work at Plas Uchaf is exceptional.

It was in the last stages of dereliction when we arrived here, but the oak frames of medieval houses are remarkably tough, particularly where they have been smoked for generations by the open hearth; and its repair was still possible, and well worth while.

The hall is surprisingly grand, with a spere truss, two other moulded trusses, traces of a louvre, and wind and ridge braces—a roof of sophisticated carpentry. In the sixteenth century an immense fireplace was added. The fire and the hall are the twin spirits of Plas Uchaf, and at night, with the wooden ribs of the hall moving a little in the firelight, you can imagine that you are Jonah inside the whale.

From the logbook

"Thank you Plas Uchaf, Landmark, Mrs. Jones, the chap for the logs, Mr. Evans the singing butcher, our farmer friend up the road who supplied fresh milk and eggs and many a chat, and farmer Tudor".

"The pubs in Cynwyd are probably open even if they look shut".

"You can't really appreciate the hall without the smell and light of the fire".

"Everyone should spend Christmas here—well, at least we should again, and perhaps will".

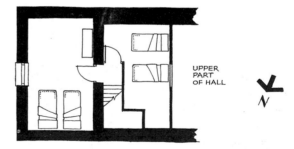

FIRST FLOOR

UPPER PART OF HALL

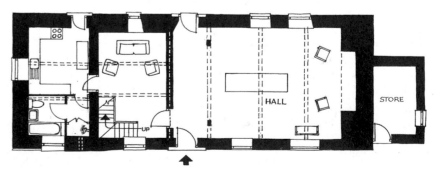

GROUND FLOOR

HALL

STORE

Poultry Cottage, Leighton, Welshpool, Powys

Leighton is a model estate on a stupendous scale, laid out in the 1850s by John Naylor, a Liverpool banker with a great deal of money to spend. Besides magnificent housing for all kinds of livestock, the estate had its own aqueduct and cable railway to take water, manure and feed to outlying farms.

The Poultry Yard was added in 1861, complete with fowl house, storm shed, pond and scratching yard; and the poultry-keeper's cottage in which you will stay. The architect was probably W. H. Gee, of Liverpool, who was also responsible for Leighton Hall and Church. The design may have been inspired by Her Majesty's Poultry Houses at Windsor, much praised in Dickson's *Poultry* of 1853. Each species, whether large or small, ornamental, water or humble hen, had its own meticulously designed quarters: a thorough attention to detail which is typical of the whole estate.

Another of Mr. Naylor's interests was forestry (the Leyland Cypress was first propagated here). Near the Poultry Yard is a grove of giant redwoods, which now belongs to the Royal Forestry Society; and the cottage is encircled by fine trees. Between them, you look across the Severn Valley to the green hills of Montgomeryshire. There, too is Powis Castle, with its hanging garden, the nearest thing that Wales has to a royal palace.

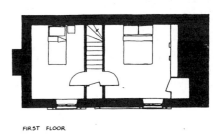

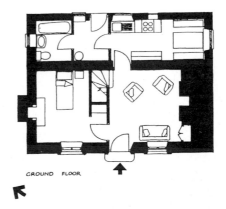

GROUND FLOOR

FIRST FLOOR

The Priest's House, Holcombe Rogus, Devon

The Priest's House should really be called the Church House, because that is what it was, half village hall and half inn. Parish feasts were held here on saints' days, and at other festivals, and hospitality was offered to guests. It had a kitchen and probably a brewery. Many church houses later became pubs, and survive as such to this day.

This one was probably built around 1500; it has fine moulded beams and a cooking hearth across one end, with another fireplace to warm the main room. By some lucky chance, it was never converted to another use, but dwindled instead into a parish store. The reason probably lies in its position, squeezed between the garden of Holcombe Court (a fine Tudor house), the stony church lane and the churchyard.

Several old windows survived and inside, where there was evidence to show they had existed, we put back oak partitions, and laid a stone floor, so that the main rooms have much the same character as they did when used for village gatherings.

Holcombe Rogus is a comfortable village in a beautiful part of Devon, close to the Somerset

border, where ancient lanes take you to unexpected, but always rewarding places. The church has a good tower, a chiming clock, and the memorable pew of the Bluett family who lived in the Court until the last century.

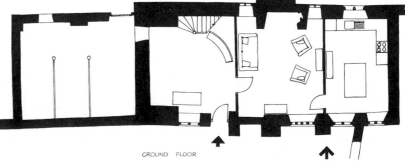

FIRST FLOOR

GROUND FLOOR

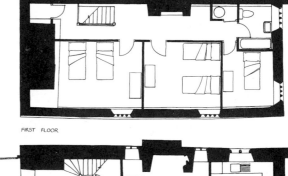

The Prospect Tower, Belmont Park, Faversham, Kent

This small flint tower stands on the very edge of the garden of Belmont Park (house remodelled by Samuel Wyatt, 1792), approached by an avenue of walnuts. On its other side is a mature park, and a now ragged cricket pitch. It was built about 1808 for General, later Lord, Harris of Seringapatam. He called it his Whim, and one suspects that the pleasant upper room, at least, was his own den, into which the family were sometimes allowed for tea.

The General bought Belmont, which owed its name to its 'high situation and extensive prospect', in 1801, with prize money won in India. Farming and gardening were his chief enthusiasms, and he soon doubled the size of the pleasure grounds to include all that part in which the tower still stands.

The enthusiasm of the 4th Lord Harris was of a different kind. He was one of the fathers of cricket, and it was he who in about 1870 created a pitch and commandeered this tower as a changing room: hooks for the gear still decorate the walls. There are only two rooms in the tower for living and sleeping, but the prospect from its windows is still extensive; and you can dream of all those centuries, hoped for and, sometimes, achieved.

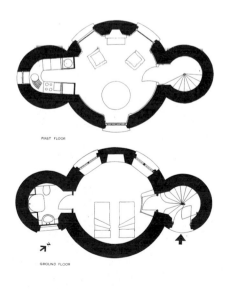

FIRST FLOOR

GROUND FLOOR

109

Purton Green, Stansfield, Suffolk

Purton Green is one of the many lost villages of Suffolk, where generations spent their lives, but which are now just patches of lime and fragments in the plough. It lies on an old road running south from Bury St. Edmunds, today hardly a path. All that remains is this house, inside whose late medieval walls there survives a hall of 1250—an extreme rarity. Aisled on both sides, with scissor-braced trusses, and a highly ornamental arcade at the low end, it must once have been an important place.

When we bought it in 1969 it was little more than a ruin. As with almost all medieval houses, a floor and central chimney stack had later been inserted, but these additions were so derelict that we felt justified in removing them, to return the hall to its original open state. Part of the house—the high end—was rebuilt about 1600 and this we have turned into living quarters.

These can only be reached through the hall, which you must cross and recross if you stay here, as your predecessors have done for seven hundred years. A car cannot be got closer than four hundred yards, and that involves crossing

a ford; but we provide a wheelbarrow for the rest of the journey ('The wheelbarrow is lovely'—Logbook). The house stands now surrounded by fields, with ordinary unchanging Suffolk countryside in all directions.

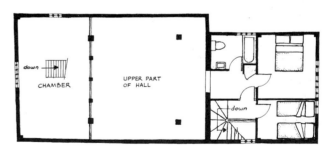

FIRST FLOOR

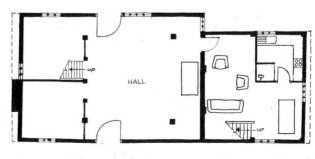

GROUND FLOOR

110

Rosslyn Castle, Roslin, Nr. Edinburgh

The St. Clairs, an ancient and important family, chose a truly dramatic site for their castle, on a tree-covered spine of rock rising steeply from the River Esk which surrounds it on three sides. It is approached on the fourth side by a high, narrow bridge across an artificial chasm.

Most of the castle was built around 1450 by the great William, Prince of Orkney, who lived at Rosslyn in regal state, dining off gold and silver. It was he who built the extraordinary ornament-encrusted chapel of St. Matthew at Roslin, one of the wonders of Scotland.

The older fortifications survive only as ruins, but shortly before 1600 Sir William Sinclair replaced the east curtain wall with a more comfortable dwelling, but one which still contains an element of drama. On one side a modest two storey building, on the other it drops five storeys down the side of the rock to reach the ground 60 feet below. Decorated with panelling and moulded plaster ceilings, but later left empty for long periods, the habitable rooms

have been restored and furnished by the present Earl of Rosslyn. To support him in his effort to keep his family's inheritance together, we let the castle on his behalf.

FIRST FLOOR

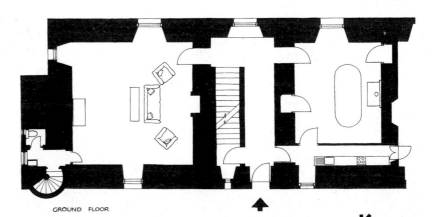

GROUND FLOOR

Rhiwddolion, Nr. Betws-y-coed, Gwynedd

Rhiwddolion is a remote upland at the head of a valley above Betws-y-coed. For a time there was a slate quarry and community here. Long before that Rhiwddolion was on the Roman road, Sarn Helen, which runs from Merioneth to the Conway valley. This Helen was mother of the Emperor Constantine, whose father campaigned and died in Britain; Edward I knew this and built Caernarvon Castle with bands of coloured stone, in imitation of Constantinople.

Now, however, Rhiwddolion, with only three houses left besides ours, is given over to the sheep. It is somewhat hemmed in by forestry, but where it remains open, the small-scale landscape of oak trees and rocks emerging from close-cropped pasture is second to none. It is also tranquil and silent except for the sheep and the water; and there is a view far down the valley towards Betws.

It is not possible to get a car to either of our houses; instead, leaving your car by the forestry track, you can walk up (10 mins., some say longer) on a path of enormous half-buried flag-stones, as your predecessors did.

Ty Capel, beside the stream which flows down the valley, was a school-cum-chapel in the days of the slate quarry. It is a robust stone building lined with varnished pine, and at the turn of the century served a community of 150 people.

From the logbook

"We came to Ty Capel with the idea of using it as a base to explore North Wales. It exercised its magic on us too, and North Wales went unexplored".

"Our children speculated for hours on the lives of the children of Rhiwddolion. We took a great delight in the mosses . . . a perfect place to get to know and understand your family".

"To my surprise I discovered that I actually quite enjoyed walking".

"The pair of elderly ladies in the Oxfam shop, Pormadoc, sang for us the Welsh hymn written by the schoolmaster of Rhiwddolion at the turn of the century".

"Ty Capel is very peaceful, the main noise being the sheep".

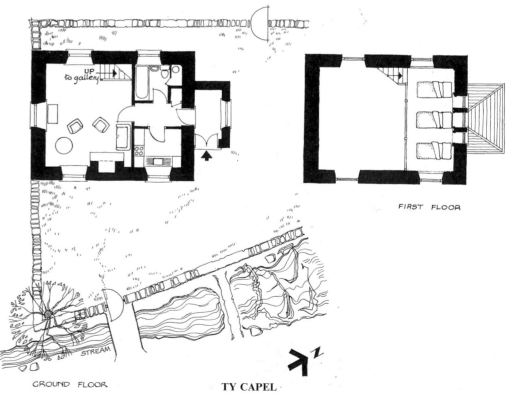

FIRST FLOOR

GROUND FLOOR   TY CAPEL

Ty Coch, which means red house, is a few hundred yards higher up, looking across the head of the valley, by a small waterfall. In origin much older than Ty Capel, it has a stone-flagged living room with a large open fireplace. The beam which spans this fireplace is a cruck, re-used no doubt from some yet earlier house that stood here.

From the logbook

"Idyllic setting, have not seen the like. Children wonderfully content to be around the waterfall and stream".

"Along Sarn Elen we found a tortoise. We took it to a cottage and found that it is Crwban in Welsh and had been lost for five months".

"We have really enjoyed the logbook. The shared experiences make us feel part of a special club".

"Every morning me and my brother William went down to the stream and played dams. I did get quite wet. In the evening I read out the logbooks".

"We've done little but achieved a lot".

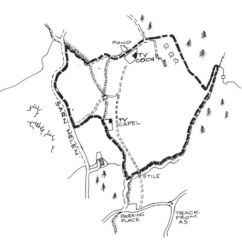

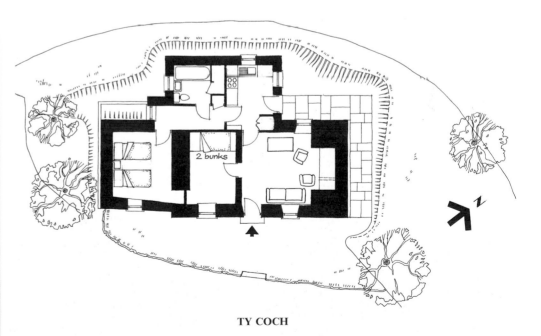

TY COCH

113

Saddell, Argyll

Saddell Castle, 'a fayre pyle, and a stronge', was built by the Bishop of Argyll in 1508. By 1600 it was firmly in the hands of the Campbells, who thereafter held it for nearly four hundred years. It is a fine and complete tower house with a battlemented wall-walk round the roof, and it stands at the mouth of a little river, looking across to Arran. When we took it on, there were substantial trees growing from the roof and all the windows had gone.

Inside, each room is quite different from all the others, and each holds something unexpected and agreeable: panelling or a decorated ceiling, deep window embrasures or closets in the thickness of the wall. The floor inside the front door is removable so that unwelcome visitors can fall straight into a pit below.

Round a narrow cobbled yard outside, the walls of the attendant outbuildings survive, including part of the old barmkin wall. Built hard up against the castle for protection, they were left because the laird never had any money to spare. Indeed all the later structural repairs seem to have been a struggle, done with whatever lay to hand, even old cart axles.

Here and there are moulded or carved stones from the ruins of Saddell Abbey, half a mile up

the valley. Under the trees in that peaceful place lie many graveslabs of the unruly Scots, gripping their long swords or standing in their ships of war, waiting for the last trumpet.

We also own the steep old beechwood behind the castle, and the whole of Saddell Bay with its long white strand and rocky point, and collection of smaller houses.

THIRD FLOOR

SECOND FLOOR

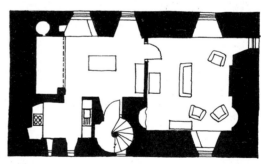

FIRST FLOOR

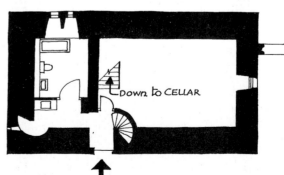

GROUND FLOOR

Down to CELLAR

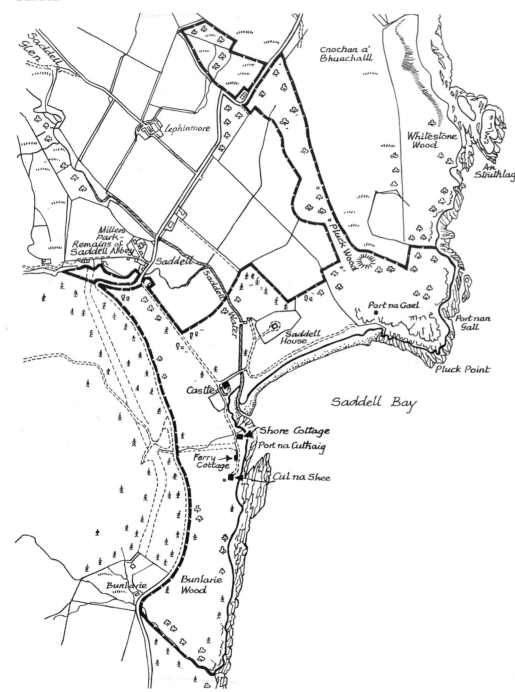

Cul na Shee means nook of peace in Gaelic, which in this case refers to a minute bay, backed by steep woods, a few hundred yards beyond the castle. Here in the 1920s the schoolteacher, daughter of a local minister, built herself a home for her retirement, on the grass behind a rocky beach. It would be hard to find a more tranquil place. It cannot be seen from anywhere and nothing can be seen from it, except the hills of Arran. It has moreover been a pleasure to preserve a building of a kind so very unfashionable now, to show how suitable it can look and how snug and cheerful its pine-boarded rooms can be.

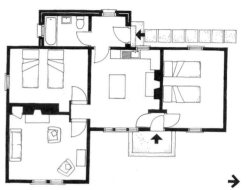

Ferry Cottage, built about 1930 on the site of a more humble predecessor, was the freehold property of an important local figure, the ferryman. Owner of a boat and a house, it was his job to offload provisions from the coastal steamer, or puffer. Before the building of good roads, much of Western Scotland was dependent on such deliveries, and Glensaddell was no exception. The house, with light-filled rooms, stands in its own garden, with the remains of a jetty in the rocky bay in front.

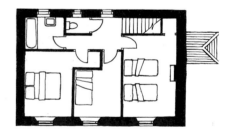

FIRST FLOOR

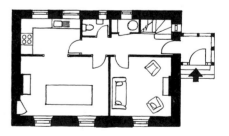

GROUND FLOOR

Shore Cottage looks at the castle across a little bay. It stands on a rocky point, among trees which grow right down to the sea, and is a plain but stylish Victorian building, imaginative in design as well as situation. From the sitting room, a door leads directly onto the foreshore, where the rockpools at low tide are second to none.

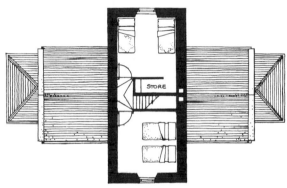

FIRST FLOOR

GROUND FLOOR

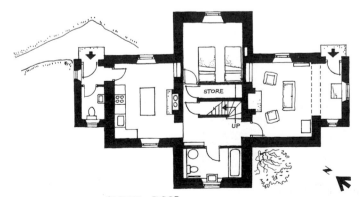

117

7 St. Michael's Street, Oxford

Oxford has more architectural pleasures and surprises than anywhere else in Britain, and nowhere else has so much spirit and energy been expended, often in marvellously silly ways. When, therefore, the Oxford Union Society needed money to repair their first debating chamber (now the library) we asked if, in return for a contribution, a place could be found where our visitors could stay.

The Union, formed as a debating society in 1823 to encourage free speech and speculation, acquired a site in St. Michael's Street in 1852. In 1856 their first debating chamber, which was to be a library as well, was built to the design of Benjamin Woodward, a disciple of Ruskin's. While he was finishing the building he showed it to D. G. Rossetti and to William Morris, 'a rather rough and unpolished youth', and they offered to paint 'figures of some kind' in the gallery window bays—which they did in the Long Vacation, assisted by their friends, including Edward Burne-Jones. William Morris finished his bay first and began painting the roof. These long-faded scenes from the Arthurian legend by famous painters in their youth, a

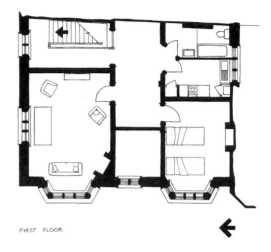

FIRST FLOOR

wonderful possession for the Union, have been brought back to life, and the building restored.

In return we have a self-contained floor and a half in the former official residence of the Steward of the Union. He was an important, permanent figure who kept the show on the road, and kept order, while generations of undergraduates came and went. His spacious house was added, with a new library, in 1910 to the design of W. E. Mills of Oxford. It is a thoroughgoing Edwardian affair, of a kind and quality which we are pleased to look after: and our generously proportioned rooms, particularly the sitting room, will give you a true impression of the Oxford of that day; while the vigorous, and sometimes rather noisy activities of modern Oxford, and the modern Union, take place outside your windows.

St. Winifred's Well, Woolston, Nr. Oswestry, Shropshire

St. Winifred was a seventh century Welsh princess, sworn to a life of chastity, who was brought back to life by her uncle, St. Beuno, after being decapitated by an angry suitor as she fled from him to take refuge in church. In the twelfth century her body was taken to Shrewsbury Abbey, where many pilgrims came to benefit from her healing miracles.

St. Winifred was soon much loved, so there is good reason to believe the tradition that this well at Woolston was dedicated to her; a lesser sister to the older and more famous St. Winifred's Well at Holywell in Flintshire.

Whether it is true or not, the well here has been venerated for centuries, and is still visited by pilgrims. The innermost of the three pools is the medieval well chamber. The little building above is the medieval well chapel, itself a miraculous survival, preserved since the Reformation as a Court House and then as a cottage. Meanwhile the well itself was enlarged to form a cold bath, first for a local squire, and later for the general public, whose conduct became so riotous that it was closed to them in 1755.

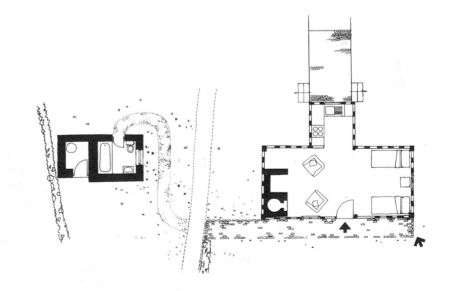

Thereafter it returned to nature, whose spirit was probably worshipped here long before Christianity. It is a secret place and hard to find, approachable only on foot. Once here, acceptance of the miraculous is easy.

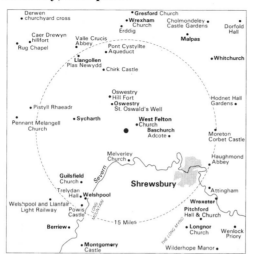

119

Shelwick Court, Hereford

For many years this house had been falling down round the head of an old farmer. It lies about three miles north-east of Hereford, beside the long-abandoned Gloucester & Hereford canal—killed as so often by the railway. Although it has a respectable stone front of about 1700, which we with some difficulty restrained from falling outwards, and a staircase of the same date, this alone would not have justified our intervention. But concealed within the house on the first floor, and indeed then made almost invisible by later alterations, lies a medieval great chamber, with a six-bay open roof of massive timbers, cusped and chamfered in the Herefordshire manner.

What is more surprising still, this roof of about 1400 and the timber framing which holds it up has clearly been moved here from somewhere else. It looks important enough to have been a hall, but there is no trace of smoke blackening, and it must have formed, it seems, the solar cross-wing to a really grand hall, perhaps on a nearby site. Whatever its origins,

it is a rare interior which has, very strongly, a life of its own. This it is a pleasure to share, even for a short time.

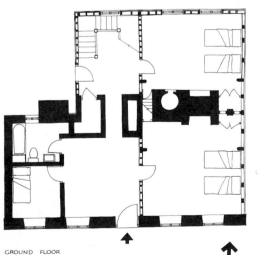

There is a single bedroom in the attic

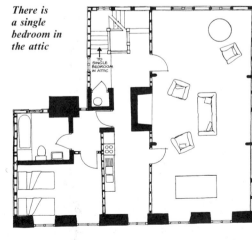

GROUND FLOOR   FIRST FLOOR

120

Shute Gatehouse, Axminster, Devon

This gatehouse, which we lease from the National Trust, was probably built by William Pole when he bought Shute in about 1560. Then it led to a large medieval and Tudor house immediately behind, now much reduced in size and known as Shute Barton. When we first saw it, the gatehouse had mouldered picturesquely for some long time, its flues and fireplaces filled with sticks by jackdaws living in the immense elms around it. Much structural work was needed, but already the weather has begun to make what we did invisible.

While the repairs were being carried out the North Devon District Council offered us a remarkable Jacobean plaster ceiling, from a house in Barnstaple demolished in the 1930s. The Council had been storing it in pieces ever since, but could do so no longer. Close in date to much of the gatehouse (which is not of a single date in any case), it fitted the upper room perfectly. So, although we would not ordinarily do such a thing, we put it up and it looks wonderful.

The elms in front of the gatehouse, which were some of the best ever seen, succumbed to

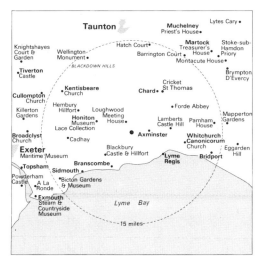

the disease; but we took advantage of this calamity to restore the ground to its original level and lay it out as a green. As a result, the gatehouse looks well from the village, and those who stay in it gain a fine view of the old deer park, particularly from the kitchen sink.

From the logbook

"The best part of the week? Seeing the gatehouse coming into view as we approached through the village, waking up to the cockerel crowing his head off in the mornings, feeling superior as people drive up to the gatehouse and get out looking impressed, hearing owls in Shute woods, and watching the bats".

"What a ceiling".

"As usual we enjoyed the car-less part of our holiday best".

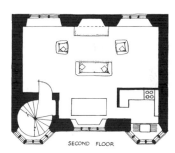

SECOND FLOOR

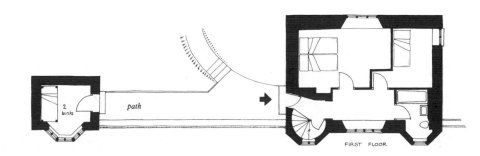

FIRST FLOOR

Stockwell Farm, Old Radnor, Powys

Behind an unassuming farmhouse front, there is here something rather earlier, to which one old roof truss in a bedroom is the clue. This belongs to a house of about 1600, which had a sleeping loft above the main living room and a door from the house to a cow byre (later a barn) under the same roof. At the other end a parlour wing was added about 1700.

One of our visitors had been here long before, as a child evacuated from wartime London, and has left a moving account in the logbook: 'Missing are the neighbours who came to stare at the new children ... Missing too the central fire, the cake hissing on the girdle ... the hideous steamy Mondays ... and the grisly boiled pig and tapioca'.

The house has a beautiful view; and behind are our own fields, into which you can turn your children, and across which you can walk up to Old Radnor. It is a quite particularly attractive hillside of rough pasture, full of mysterious hollows, green hummocks, anthills, thorn bushes and other unfunctional things.

Old Radnor consists of a few scattered cot-

tages, a fine fifteenth century church containing the oldest organ case in Britain, and the Harp Inn which we once owned and restored. Charles I is known to have been here since he complained about the food.

From the logbook

"We would love to return here: the lack of clutter is a pleasure to experience".

"The vicar called on horseback".

"For botanists; there is a very good bog at Tregaron".

"We have found Stockwell Farm charming ... We would love to come again but it is a long way from Adelaide".

"We have enjoyed the farm and the insight it gives one into the lives of our ancestors".

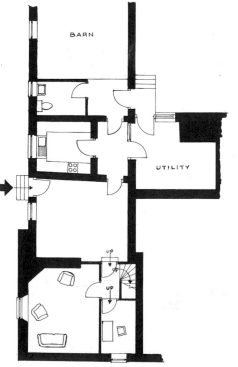

GROUND FLOOR

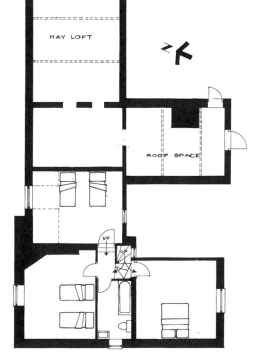

FIRST FLOOR

Stogursey Castle, Nr. Bridgwater, Somerset

Stogursey, an old village to the east of the Quantocks, was chosen as his principal base by William de Courcy, Steward to Henry I. Both his son and his grandson married heiresses and the de Courcys became even more important. So too did their castle. Then the male line failed, and the castle was inherited by Alice de Courcy. She entertained King John here in 1210, when her husband won 20 shillings from him 'at play'.

Later on the Percys from Northumberland inherited it but, after a minor part in the Wars of the Roses, there was no very useful purpose that it could serve as it stood and they did not think it worth rebuilding as a less fortified seat. So time and neglect, and adaptation to more humble uses, reduced it to ruins, in which it has lain ever since.

The small dwelling formed inside the gate towers of the castle has seventeenth century roof timbers and was repaired in the 1870s; but when we found it, the entire castle had vanished beneath a mantle of vegetation. Clearing this and dredging the moat revealed an unsuspected thirteenth century bridge. We also recovered some chain mail and other warlike fragments from the mud. The cottage makes a strange dwelling but a pleasant one, still commanding the only entrance to the castle's grassy inner ward, scene of all these doings long ago.

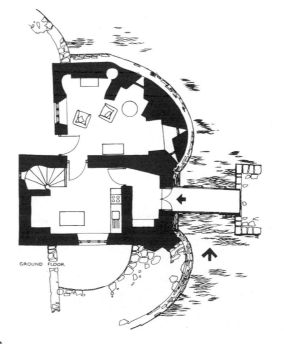

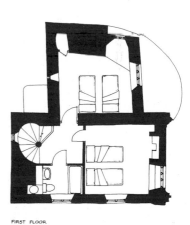

GROUND FLOOR

FIRST FLOOR

123

The Swarkestone Pavilion, Nr. Ticknall, Derbyshire

The excuse for building this majestic little pavilion was to give a grandstand view of whatever went on in the enclosure in front of it. Suggestions range from the romantic (jousting) and the rough (bear-baiting) to the more prosaic (bowls). Evidence supports the latter, with a payment in 1632 for a 'bowle alley house'. It was built by a mason, Richard Shepperd, but its design has been attributed to John Smythson, one of our first true architects and son of the great Robert. So, whatever its purpose, it is a building well worth preserving.

Swarkestone Hall was demolished by 1750. The pavilion survived, and was maintained by that most conserving of families, the Harpur Crewes of Calke Abbey, but it had long been a shell when we bought it. We reroofed it and put back floors and windows, to recreate the upstairs room in which you will live and sleep. The bathroom is in the top of one of the turrets, above the kitchen, and to reach it you must cross the open roof—an unlooked for opportunity to study the sky at night.

Swarkestone, with its important bridge across the Trent, has seen great events: a battle for its

control in the Civil War did great damage to the Hall; and in 1745 it was the point at which Bonnie Prince Charlie recognised the futility of his attempt on the English throne, and turned his troops back towards Scotland, to meet their fate at Culloden.

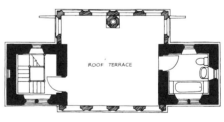

SECOND FLOOR

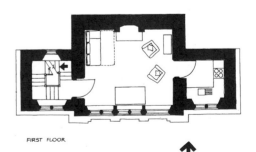

FIRST FLOOR

124

Tangy Mill, Kintyre, Argyll

Towards the south end of Kintyre, on the western side, the landscape changes and there is a broad, open sweep of fertile land. Tangy Mill was built about 1820, probably on the site of an earlier mill, to serve the big arable farms here. It stands in beautiful surroundings on the north bank of the Tangy Burn, near the point where it enters the sea, and is made of harled whinstone with sandstone dressings. For our repairs we obtained more of this sandstone from the original quarry.

Because of the climate the corn (mostly oats) had to be dried before grinding, and there is a two-storey kiln with a big revolving ventilator, known as a 'granny', on its roof. Here the oats were spread 6 inches deep on the perforated iron floor of what is now one of the bedrooms. The mill had been disused for ten years when we bought it, but the dressing, drying, hoisting and grinding machinery, the stones and shutes and the backshot wheel, were still there; we have kept all this in position and amongst it you live and sleep. The atmosphere of old places of work is almost impossible to preserve, because one cannot preserve old workmen and old ways of life; but this mill was so complete and in such an unexpected place that here for once we have attempted it.

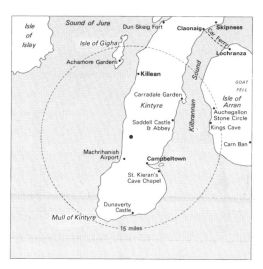

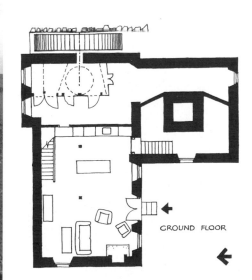

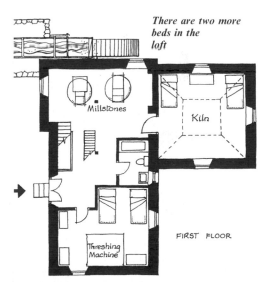

There are two more beds in the loft

Millstones

Kiln

GROUND FLOOR

Threshing Machine

FIRST FLOOR

125

Tewkesbury, Gloucestershire

30 and 32 St Mary's Lane are two eighteenth century framework knitters' cottages in a lane leading down to the Avon. A third next to them we gave, when restored, to the local preservation society. The stocking makers both lived and worked here, in what was then the town's chief industry. The workshops were on the first floor (now sitting rooms) with long windows for the light. From them can be seen the marvellous roofscape of Tewkesbury, backing onto the river, and there is a fine view of the Abbey along the narrow court behind.

Tewkesbury is an exceptional town, with many medieval and Tudor buildings. These did not reach this century without some help from the restorers of the last; indeed, it is to Gilbert Scott's proposals for the Abbey, that tremendous fane, that we owe the birth of the Society for the Protection of Ancient Buildings in 1877.

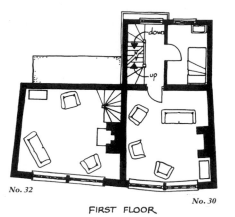

No. 32   No. 30
FIRST FLOOR

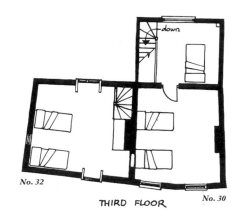

No. 32   No. 30
THIRD FLOOR

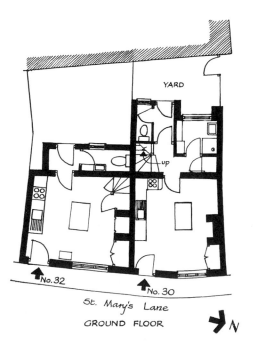

No. 32   No. 30
St. Mary's Lane
GROUND FLOOR   N

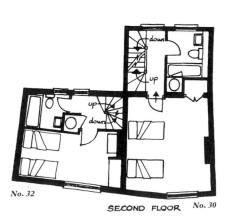

No. 32
SECOND FLOOR   No. 30

126

Tewkesbury

Once established in Tewkesbury, we were offered a lease of the **Abbey Gatehouse**, a grand building of about 1500, restored in 1849 by J. Medland. His work was thorough but skilful—indeed it is difficult to tell now just how much of the stonework he renewed. The gatehouse has only one room, a very fine one on the first floor, and at one end of this we have built a gallery, rather like an organ case. Inside it there is everything that you need, but do not want to see; and on its top you sleep, close under the moulded beams of the roof. These are painted in the same colours as the vault of the choir in the Abbey itself, a wonderful church, whose soaring west window rises only a few yards from your door, as you dwell in the 'lodging over the great gate'.

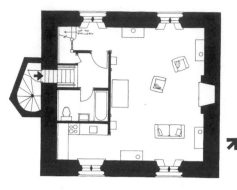

FIRST FLOOR

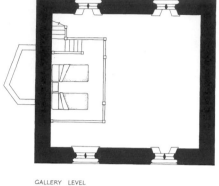

GALLERY LEVEL

128

The Tower, Canons Ashby, Northamptonshire

The last time that Canons Ashby was altered in any major way was in 1710. Thereafter, its owners, the Drydens, matched their tastes and needs to those of their house, living with Elizabethan and Jacobean decoration and furniture, all of great charm and interest.

In 1980, the house was transferred to the National Trust, after a public appeal to raise the funds needed to endow and restore it. We contributed to the restoration fund, to set the ball rolling, and offered to pay for the creation and repair of one flat.

Accordingly we were given the top of the sixteenth century tower, where there were formerly two bedrooms, reached by a newel stair with solid oak treads. We tidied up these light and pleasant rooms, which look down the axis of the garden; and put a bathroom and kitchen in two adjoining attics. A new dormer window was made to light the kitchen, which is invisible from below but provides an agreeable view of the roofs from the sink.

Meanwhile the quiet building below has come back to life, and is open to the public from

April to October—and to you, free of charge, within normal opening times when you stay here. And at the end of the day, when the last visitor has gone, you can enjoy the privilege of an owner and walk in the garden undisturbed.

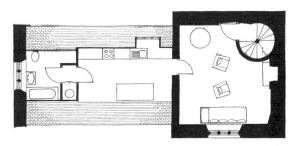

From the top of the tower

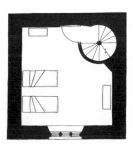

SECOND FLOOR

TOWER ROOM

129

Tixall Gatehouse, Nr. Stafford

As the traveller by canal comes down the valley of the Sow, and through Tixall lock, he enters the last and most beautiful mile of the Staffordshire & Worcestershire canal. The cut here broadens into a lake, known to boaters as Tixall Wide. On either side lie most handsome stretches of country—Shugborough to the south, and, to the north, Ingestre, with Tixall Gatehouse in the foreground. This was built about 1580 by Sir Walter Aston, whose son had just married the daughter of Sir Thomas Lucy (Shakespeare's Justice Shallow) of Charlecote, where an earlier gatehouse may have inspired the much grander one at Tixall.

The Tudor house, in front of which the gatehouse stood, was replaced in 1780 by another built to one side of it by Thomas Clifford, a descendant of the Astons. In this, and in his landscape works, he was guided by 'the celebrated Brown' and his pupil, Eames. Both houses have disappeared, and the gatehouse today is surrounded by grass. It was described by Erdeswick in 1598 as 'one of the fairest pieces of work made of late times that I have seen in all these counties' and, more recently, as 'an Elizabethan ruin, without roof,

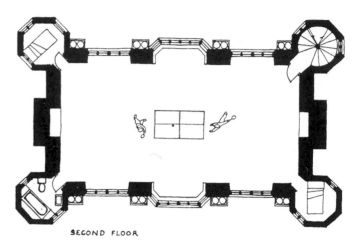

floors or windows, standing in a field and used as a shelter for cattle'.

We bought the building for £300 in 1968. The first floor we divided into five large rooms, one of them a gallery with an oriel window at each end above the two archways. In the spandrels of these archways are, facing the outside world,

armed warriors; and, on the inside, voluptuous ladies thinly disguised as angels. The second floor we left empty.

The roof is paved with stone, and to be high up here among the balustrades and turret tops, with Arcadian landscape on every hand, is yet another important Landmark Trust experience. The gatehouse clock lives in one of the turrets; this strikes the hour and perhaps the half-hour, but has no hands or face to show the actual

time, which here seems unimportant, even vulgar.

Mary, Queen of Scots, victim of her fatal inheritance, was imprisoned here for a fortnight in 1586. Thirty years later her son James I came here for two days. In 1678 Tixall, by then a Catholic house, played a part in the Titus Oates conspiracy; the Aston of the day was sent to the Tower and Lord Stafford, accused of plotting at Tixall, was executed.

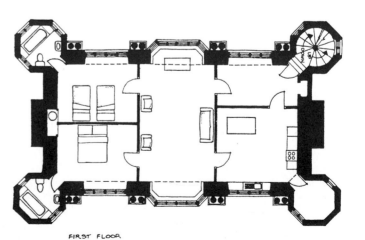

SECOND FLOOR

FIRST FLOOR

130

15 Tower Hill, St. David's, Pembrokeshire

This modern cottage occupies a most important site. It is built just above the close wall at St. David's, and has an astonishing view of the cathedral, facing it squarely at tower level. To arrive here is to feel that you have completed a pilgrimage, drawn down the long Pembrokeshire peninsular towards a place of worship that was already ancient when the Normans built their cathedral beside it. There is still much of the monastery here, both in the actual buildings that survive, and their sense of enclosure within the valley; and in the warmth of their welcome when finally you top the last hill, and pass between the last houses, to obtain your first full view of them.

The cottage living room has great serenity, with the sun on one side, and the sunlit cathedral on the other. The furniture is very good. Here little need trouble you ('A snail ate a vital part of my message to the milkman'—Logbook) and at your door is the reassurance of cathedral life, its services, the bells, and the building itself. The sea is about a mile away in

most directions; the coastal path, with stunning views, encircles St. David's—'a long way, but very good for you'.

Tower Hill Lodge, Llanarthney, Dyfed

We acquired this building as part of a joint scheme with the National Trust to preserve Paxton's Tower and its surroundings. It is an early nineteenth century cottage of well above average quality, built for the tower's caretaker, looking south over an immense expanse of country. It is difficult to imagine a finer view. If however you walk a hundred yards or so up the small green hill behind, to the foot of the Tower, there in the opposite direction the finer view is—surely one of the best in Britain, a prospect extensive and rich, embracing the whole vale of the Tywi, whose green windings your eye can follow for thirty miles or more.

Paxton's Tower itself was built about 1811, to designs by S. P. Cockerell, ostensibly as a memorial to Nelson but also as an eyecatcher for Middleton Hall, now demolished. Our cottage has rather a modern interior, but an interesting arrangement and a handsome attic.

From the logbook

"If you enjoy beautiful countryside and incredible silence then we think you will enjoy Tower Hill Lodge as we have done".

"On Wednesday morning nine deer were in the wood next to the cottage".

"... the farmer rounding up his sheep on stout mountain pony with aid of whistle and those highly intelligent dogs, fascinating to watch".

"Have heard a nightingale most evenings".

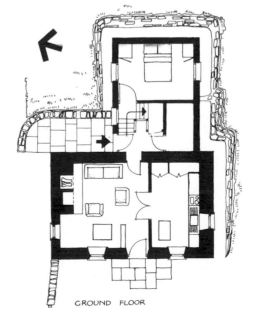

GROUND FLOOR

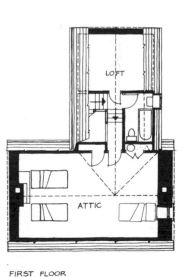

FIRST FLOOR

133

Villa Saraceno, Vicenza, Italy

Few architects have influenced Western architecture more than the Renaissance Italian, Andrea Palladio. Moreover the Palladian villa we have taken on here exemplifies everything that English architects, especially, learned from him. Begun before 1550, it was built for Biagio Saraceno, a minor noble from Vicenza, and was for him both country retreat and working farm.

It was planned with colonnaded barns around a courtyard, but only the main house was built. Nearly all the other buildings in the group are of earlier date, including the simple early Renaissance house in which most of you will sleep. Some, like the colonnaded barn which links the two houses, were rebuilt later. After many years of neglect all the buildings were decayed, some ruinous. It has taken an enormous amount of work to repair them.

Inside the main house, inserted walls have come down to recreate the original arrangement, of a grand *sala* with two-room apartments opening off it, and huge granaries above. Dim frescoed friezes have been cleaned to reveal scenes of high drama, painted probably in the 1580s or '90s for Biagio's son.

Little over an hour from Venice, the villa stands in a plain to the west of the Euganean

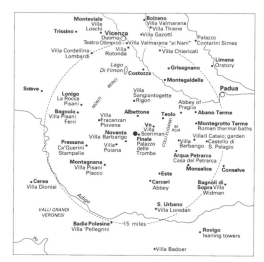

Hills. A country of poplars and canals, agriculture and now some industry, it has always been wealthy. Each small town nearby boasts a great villa, some in active use. There is little preparation for tourists, except in the true sense, of leaving it to you to make discoveries.

Parts of the villa are open to the public on Wednesday afternoons.

The South front before repairs to the plaster

Detail from the frescoed frieze in the sala

The repaired North front

134

UPPER PART OF
DRAWING ROOM

UPPER PART
OF SALA

UPPER PART
OF BEDROOM

GRANARY

BARCHESSA   SECOND FLOOR   CASA VECCHIA

UPPER PART OF
KITCHEN HALL

UPPER PART OF
GARDEN ROOM

LOGGIA AT GROUND
FLOOR LEVEL

ENTRANCE
FROM LOGGIA BELOW

BARCHESSA   FIRST FLOOR   CASA VECCHIA

PIANO
NOBILE

N

GROUND FLOOR
CASA VECCHIA

Warden Abbey, Nr. Biggleswade, Bedfordshire

Warden Abbey was Cistercian, founded in 1135. It was dissolved in 1537 and a large house was built on the site by the Gostwick family. The seal of the abbey on the deed of surrender bears St. Mary with the infant Christ standing on her knee. On the counter-seal is a crozier between three Warden pears.

Nothing remains above ground of house or abbey except this puzzling fragment, of which we have a long lease. It stands near a big farm, in a meadow made uneven by what lies underneath, and is an extremely perplexing building, of very high quality. Clearly it formed part of the Gostwick's house, but it also incorporates part of the abbey; in the course of our repairs a fourteenth century tile pavement emerged, one of the finest ever discovered, which you can see for yourselves in Bedford Museum.

The principal room downstairs seems to have been part of a gallery or broad corridor, with a large open fireplace added to one end. Occupying the entire first floor is a single room with a Tudor fireplace, an oriel window, and a heavily moulded oak ceiling. It is a pleasure to lie here in bed and wonder for whom such a splendid room can have been constructed: for one of the last abbots; for his guests; or for the Gostwicks? Above again is a superb attic, in which one visitor put her three aunts, uproariously sharing a room for the first time since childhood.

The surrounding country has had the advantage of belonging to large landowners and is some of the best in Bedfordshire.

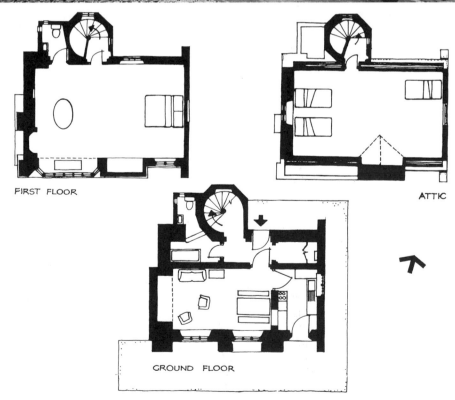

FIRST FLOOR

ATTIC

GROUND FLOOR

136

The Wardrobe, The Close, Salisbury, Wiltshire

In return for our help with rehousing their museum in the Wardrobe (which had been empty for some time and needed expensive repairs), the Berkshire and Wiltshire Regiment allowed us to form a flat in the attics. Here, approached by a seventeenth century staircase, are three lofty rooms, each with a different outlook. The Landmark prides itself on the views from its many windows, but the view from the sitting room here of the cathedral is one of the best of all, whether by day or by night, when it seems to be floodlit expressly for one's benefit.

The Wardrobe, which contains traces of a substantial medieval hall, was at some early date the Bishop's storehouse, and so got its name. Since before 1600 it has been a house, mostly let by the Dean & Chapter to laymen, who formed in it some very handsome rooms which are now part of the museum. One family, the Husseys, must have used our attics as nurseries, since during our building work we discovered toys, and even a manuscript novel by a thirteen year old Victorian daughter.

All cathedral closes have a special quality,

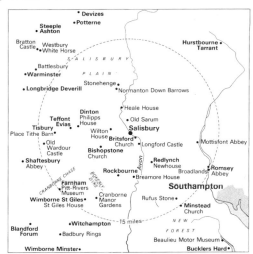

but this is one of the very best, a succession of beautiful houses ranged round the only English cathedral built at one go; and behind the Wardrobe a long walled garden, which those who stay here may use, runs down to the swift and silent Avon at its end.

From the logbook

"We climbed the stairs and the Cathedral became ours for a week—choirs rehearsing evensong, the doves, the laughter of children on the green, the sound of cricket bats, bells ringing the changes . . . just listen."

"The Saturday market yielded some highly recommended lemon curd from the W.I. stall."

"A must is to read Golding's *The Spire*, then go on the roof tour of the Cathedral."

"Even on the short journey from bedroom to bathroom I could not resist a detour to make sure the view was still there."

"We will never forget the week spent under Salisbury spire."

From the sitting room

ATTIC FLAT

The West Blockhouse, Dale, Pembrokeshire

This is the outermost work of the mid-nineteenth century fortification of Milford Haven. It had a single battery of six heavy guns commanding the entrance to the harbour, with defensible barracks behind to give protection from attack on the landward side. The fort was completed in 1857 and contained accommodation for a garrison of 34 men and one officer. It continued in use until after the Second World War, updated from time to time with new guns and new emplacements.

The walls of finely dressed limestone are of exceptional quality (as too were the repairs to them). The size of the granite coping stones on the parapet of the battery itself will astonish even those familiar with Victorian ideas of how a job should be done. The Victorians also knew how to make themselves comfortable: inside, the rooms on the first floor are lined with thick pine boards so that, with the coal fire burning, you are cosily remote from the elements.

It is a vertiginous spot, but the view down the coast of Pembrokeshire is one to savour. Victorian fortification and twentieth century industry

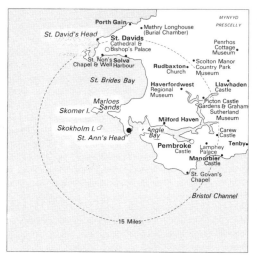

alike are dwarfed and absorbed. And there is still, occasionally, the spectacle of a big ship feeling its way into the mouth of the haven at one's feet. In contrast, there is a sheltered, south-facing beach within a few hundred yards.

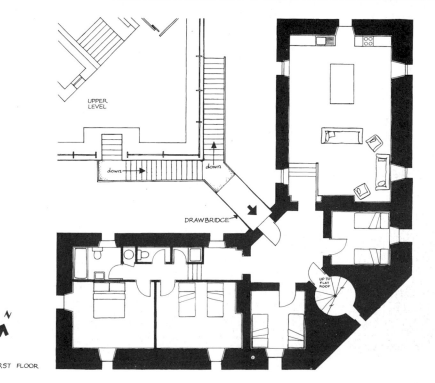

UPPER LEVEL

DRAWBRIDGE

UP TO FLAT ROOF

FIRST FLOOR

138

The White House, Aston Munslow, Shropshire

This was long the home of Miss Constance Purser, who nurtured it and uncovered its past, and built up a collection of household and agricultural implements, while opening to the public in a small way. In 1990 she passed the house and its contents on to us.

Until 1945, the White House belonged to the Stedmans, who had lived here from soon after 1300 in nearly unbroken line. The tops of great cruck trusses can be seen in the roof space. Below are rooms of Tudor and Jacobean date, with wide oak floorboards and a pleasing jumble of different windows. After a fire in 1780, a polite new drawing room was added at one end, with a bedroom above.

The house stands on the south side of Wenlock Edge, and the garden runs down the hill in front, with long views of Corvedale towards Ludlow, capital of the Marches. Just below is the village of Aston Munslow. Behind the house are outbuildings of all shapes and dates and sizes, many containing equipment appropriate to their original use.

From the logbook

"We took a tarpaulin onto the lawn and lay on our backs to watch the shooting stars".

"Proved to be an excellent place for sardines (the game), Cowboys and Indians, and especially treasure hunts".

"We have left one of our party in the secret room".

"The Swan Inn has a fantastic fancy dress party every Thursday night; its well worth dressing up and dropping in".

FIRST FLOOR

GROUND FLOOR

Whiteford Temple, Nr. Callington, Cornwall

The Duchy of Cornwall generously gave us this handsome granite building. It was put up in 1799 for Sir John Call, a military engineer who made a fortune in India. By 1770, at the age of 38, he was able to retire, marry, and build himself here a substantial mansion. This, with the estate, was sold to the Duchy in 1879. The house was largely demolished in 1913, and today all that remains are traces of its garden, part of the stables, and this temple, on its own, high above.

It is not clear how it was reached from the house, how its surroundings were laid out, nor how it was used—though its three arches were certainly glazed at one time. Accounts of a party held in it in 1847 make one suppose that it must then have been larger; and also that it was nearer to the house, so perhaps it has been moved. It had become a shelter for cattle when we first saw it, with a roof of corrugated iron and a floor of earth.

It has a fine open view, looking towards the estuary of the Tamar in the distance; and it is well designed, an ornament in the landscape

which it would be sad to lose. Accordingly, we restored it, as a single large room with two small wings, which is our best guess at what its unknown architect intended.

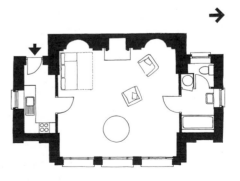

141

Woodsford Castle, Nr. Dorchester, Dorset

What remains here is one side of a small quadrangular castle, licensed in 1335 and completed about 1370. The grand apartment and lesser lodgings that make up the existing building were the work of Guy de Bryan, a close friend and servant of King Edward III, who bought the castle in 1367. Defence is just beginning to give way to a more domestic way of life; but although the hall and the chapel next to it have large windows in the outer walls, they are still up on the first floor, over vaulted kitchens and store rooms.

When we acquired it, the castle had passed by inheritance for over six hundred years. Two of its owners, the Earls of Ormonde and Devon, were executed in succession during the Wars of the Roses. It then went by marriage to the Strangways, fell into decay, and became a farmhouse—an enormous roof of thatch replacing the original turrets and crenellations. Meanwhile, the other three sides of the castle gradually disappeared, their stone put to more useful purpose elsewhere.

Inside, among much other work, we have restored the King's Room, or hall, and given it a new oak ceiling. This, with the chapel and the adjoining Queen's Room, form the main rooms in which you will stay. Kitchen, and more bedrooms, are in an eighteenth century wing on the north-west corner.

An earlier restoration in 1850 was carried out by the builder father of Thomas Hardy, and Hardy himself came here often. It is indeed a prime spot for those who like his books. The castle stands on the right bank of the Frome, three miles below Dorchester, and the north window of the hall looks out across the river and water meadows to the high ground of Egdon Heath. All this is his stage; here Hardy's characters act out their narrow parts—against a backdrop of the Universe.

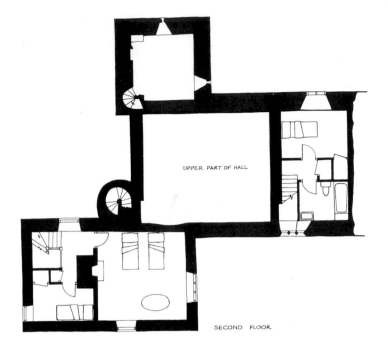

SECOND FLOOR

There is a second bathroom on the ground floor

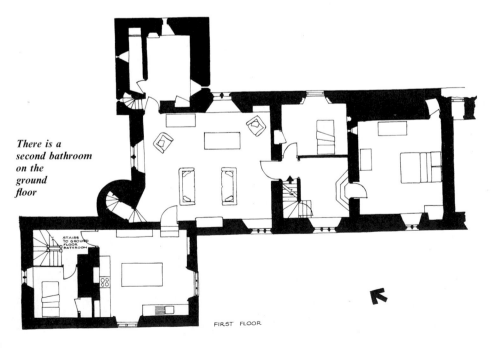

FIRST FLOOR

143

Woodspring Priory, Weston-super-Mare, Avon

We bought Woodspring Priory in 1969, when the National Trust acquired the coastal land near it. The priory was founded in 1210, perhaps as an expiatory gesture, by William de Courtenay, grandson of Reginald FitzUrse who, with other West Countrymen, murdered Thomas Becket. It was an Augustinian house, of the rule of St. Victor, dedicated to the Trinity, St. Mary and St. Thomas the Martyr.

Woodspring does not seem to have flourished except, as elsewhere in Somerset, during the fifteenth century, when the tower and nave of the church, the infirmary and the great barn were built of a beautiful golden stone. The north aisle was unfinished when, in 1536, the priory was suppressed and the church, most unusually, turned into a house, its chimney-stack built up through the roof of the nave.

We found Woodspring as it had been since the Dissolution, the church still inhabited as the farmhouse of a picturesque and rather old-fashioned farm. However, the buildings had suffered greatly from the ravages of time. We repaired the church tower (one man and a boy, using ladders) and reinstated the crossing and north aisle inside it. These we opened to the public (daylight hours, never closed). At the same time, we repaired the infirmary, which we

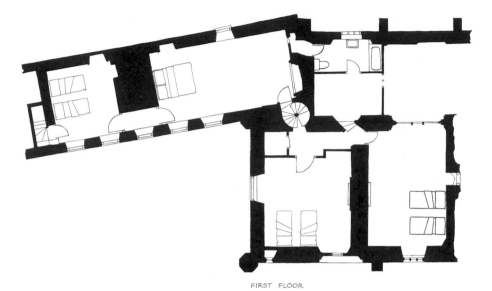

FIRST FLOOR

left as we found it, with an earth floor, and open to sheep and cattle; removed many sheds, poles and wires; and de-modernised an old cottage for our curator.

Some years later, we began the task of making the priory habitable for visitors. The farmhouse range of 1701 was re-roofed and its floors and windows repaired, along with the great fireplace of the prior's lodging found within it.

Two large bedrooms and the sitting room occupy the nave of the church, each containing some token of its ecclesiastical past. Their windows look onto south-facing walled gardens, once the cloister and the outer court.

Other monastic remains are grander, others more complete than Woodspring, but few have kept so well the serene atmosphere of an isolated religious community, surrounded by a working farm, and lying by the sea.

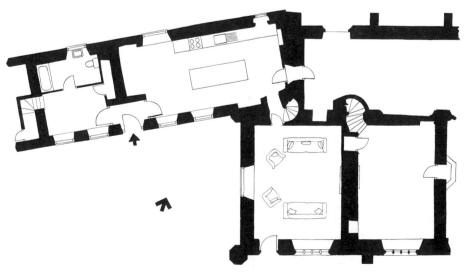

GROUND FLOOR

145

Wortham Manor, Lifton, Devon

This is a medieval and Tudor house of the highest quality, built and then remodelled by a junior branch of the great Devon family of Dinham, but little altered since. Doors and windows are of finely dressed granite, a noble if intractable material seen to great advantage here.

The chamber over the hall has an open arch-braced roof, less massive but otherwise very like that in the great hall at Cotehele, further down the Tamar valley. The hall itself has a ceiling of heavily moulded oak beams and rich late Gothic carving. Both are close in date, and may even have been put up together soon after 1500. Most probably, along with the carved surround of the front door, they are the work of John Dinham, cousin of Dame Thomasine of Week St. Mary, whose building work at the College (see p. 24) he oversaw. Like her, he had lived, and prospered, in London. In 1533, when an old man, he was pressed to take a knighthood, but declined.

Along with much other work, the house had to be entirely re-roofed, which gave us the opportunity to recover its original plan. We also bought the disused farm buildings on two sides

of the house so that its setting could be preserved as well. Those who stay here have an unrivalled opportunity to experience the life of a prosperous, and quite sophisticated, Tudor gentleman, in that distant part of Devon once known as Cornwall in England.

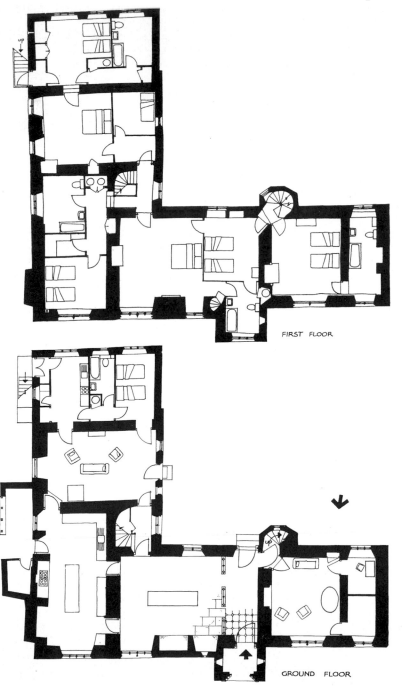

FIRST FLOOR

GROUND FLOOR

146

147

Future Landmarks

The Coop House at Netherby, near Carlisle, stands right on the bank of the Esk. It has been abandoned since 1936, and looked a lost cause, being reachable only on foot. But its owner gave us a lease and a track will soon be laid, allowing the builders to start work.

It was probably built in the 1770s to grace the end of a great stone weir, in front of which were salmon coops or traps. The remains of these and of the weir are strewn on the river bed, like relics of an ancient civilisation, but dating in fact from the 1760s.

The Netherby estate was carved out of the Debateable Lands after 1600 by Sir Richard Graham of Esk, whose numerous family had long held the area from Scots, English and each other. When Dr. Robert Graham inherited in 1757, he set about making improvements. The weir was one of his more ambitious schemes, but failed, because the river repeatedly broke it up. It had also proved unpopular with the Scots upriver who, deprived of their catch, marched in strength on Netherby, causing the Grahams to be called to arms for the last time to defend their property.

Elton House overlooks Abbey Green, in the centre of Bath. It was given to us, with much desirable furniture, by Miss Philippa Savery, a gallant campaigner for the city's preservation. In 1946, she had rented one room here, for a shop, the rest of the house being occupied by a cobbler and twelve other tenants. Then, as more rooms fell empty, Miss Savery took them over and in 1962 she bought the freehold. Until age prevented her, she cared for and occupied the house with great resourcefulness and ingenuity, always on a shoestring.

The earliest part of it dates from just before 1700, but subsequently it was enlarged and refronted, becoming by 1750 a handsome, robust building, with a fine staircase and excellent joinery, arranged as sets of lodgings. Thereafter the fashionable world began to move up the hill, away from Abbey Green; part of the ground floor of Elton House became a shop, and the rest of the interior was never altered again. It is therefore something of a rarity, even for Bath. Work is now in progress to adapt the upper floors as a Landmark, with a shop below.

Future Landmarks

Crownhill Fort, Plymouth, was the key to the landward defences of the naval base, and is one of only two large works of this kind in the country to remain unaltered and in good condition. It was completed in 1868 and was continuously occupied by the Army until 1986.

It was designed for 32 guns, of which the largest were to be in barbettes and Haxo casemates. Outside the steep defensive scarp is a deep dry ditch thirty feet wide at the bottom, excavated in the solid rock. This is protected by a partially enclosed chemin de ronde and six three storey caponnieres reached from inside the fort by long underground tunnels. Round the central parade ground are a huge magazine, and handsome quarters for 300 officers and men.

Since acquiring the fort in 1987, we have concentrated on the grounds, clearing tunnels and walkways, and correcting levels and profiles throughout this spectacular structure of stone and earth. Work has now begun to prepare the fort for regular opening to the public. At the same time we shall be making a Landmark in the officers' quarters, to be ready in 1995.

The Officers' Quarters

Future Landmarks

Houghton West Lodge, in Norfolk, lies just off the great West Avenue, the longest of all those that radiate from Houghton Hall, Sir Robert Walpole's splendid rural palace. It is small and neat, built around a central chimney, with an enclosed yard and shed at the back. It once had trellis-work gates and fences which we plan to renew.

Neither this lodge, nor the similar North and East Lodges, formed part of the estate improvements to which the great Georgian Prime Minister devoted so much energy and care. The work of Repton or Loudon, rather than Palladio, provided the model for their design, because they were not built until the 1840s. They replaced earlier lodges which for some reason proved unsatisfactory.

West Lodge has been empty for some years, and since it is no longer needed by the estate, was offered to us. It stands in woods, set back from a country lane, by a drive that is now scarcely used. Its repair has had to wait on the completion of other buildings, but we hope its turn will come in 1994. The opportunity to stay so agreeably at the nobleman's gate is not to be missed.

Obriss Farm, near Westerham in Kent, sits on the lower slopes of Toys Hill, looking South over the Weald. It was given to us by the executors of Mrs Helena Cooper—160 acres, mainly of pasture, with some woods, and at the centre, well away from any roads, a compact group of buildings which, with their mixture of brick and timber and tile, fit comfortably into the landscape. The field pattern here has not changed since 1840 and probably before.

Besides the farmhouse, in which you will stay, and a smokehouse behind it with a tall chimney, all the traditional buildings are here: byres, stable and sheds round the yard in front of the house, and off to one side the great threshing barn, which shows that the farming was once more mixed than it is now. Behind the house are the remains of once flourishing orchards, awaiting replanting.

Work will start on the house as soon as we can raise the funds for it. The farm is let to a sheep-farmer, and plans are afoot for the woods—some to be coppiced, others left well alone. To have this activity going on gently around you through the seasons will be part of the pleasure and interest of staying here.

Future Landmarks

28 South Street, Great Torrington, was a wealthy merchant's house, built in 1701. For nearly the first time in Devon, the main ground floor rooms were for the family, instead of for trade. They lie on either side of the front door, with a hall between leading to a fine staircase—a symmetry which was also new.

The real pleasure of the house lies not in the groping towards metropolitan high fashion, however, nor even in the long garden behind, but in the plasterwork of one ceiling and the shell hood over the front door. A school of plasterers had long existed in Devon, producing work of exceptional quality. One of the finest of them was employed here, to model with crispness and clarity trophies of arms and musical instruments, with foliage and stout mouldings.

Although built and long occupied by prominent citizens, its freehold belonged to an ancient charity which owned much of the town. In recent years an office, but deserving better, it was suggested and sold to us by the Trustees. When completed in 1995 it will offer the now rare experience of living in quite a grand house in the street of a country town—of which Torrington is a very agreeable example.

Silverton Park Stables are near Broadclyst in Devon, a theatrical building in a theatrical setting. To start with, you enter the park by turning off the road on the wrong side; then, following the drive round a steep curve, you pass through a tunnel, to emerge into one of those mysterious landscapes of fine trees and gently graded slopes that announce the site of a vanished house. Directly in front of you are the stables, looking like a backdrop from Aida.

Silverton Park itself was an immense Grecian palace, designed by T.H. Knowles and built between 1839 and 1845 for the 4th Earl of Egremont. The interior was never completed, however, and in 1900 the house was demolished.

The stable block survived. A quadrangle with four porticoes, this was as ambitious as the main house, and like it was designed to be rendered in a Patent Metallic Sand Cement, but it seems that this, too, was never completed. For many years it has been a farm, with a house in one corner. In 1986 it came up for sale with plans for conversion to four houses. This seemed a pity, so we bought it, and when Philip Ford's building team have finished at South Street, Torrington, we hope to bring them here.

151

Acknowledgements

Photographs:

Archive 12,59;
Richard Barnett vi,vii;
Andrew Besley 35;
Alice Boyd 30,36,62,63;
Nicholas Breach 60;
A. S. Brindley 131;
Browning Institute 16;
J. Bucknall 11,148;
A. R. Bultitude 112;
M. Campbell-Cole
viii,ix,x,13,18,19,33,44,63,94,95,104;
Fiona Cameron 103;
D. Carpenter 25,26;
Robert Chapman 66,67,141
O. F. Clarke
20,38,68,69,71,72,73,75,77,126,127,132,139;
Country Life 23,64;
B. Cutler 78;
C. Dalton 120;
Derby Museums ii;
P. Douglas-Hamilton
4,5,6,7,14,15,17,52,80,98,99,105,111,114,115,
116,117,125,148;
R. Evans 25;
J. Evetts
xii,10,24,30,36,63,64,75,81,87,89,102,108,118,
122,124,125,133,136,137;
J. Ewers 39;
R. Farley ix;
Simon Ferguson 84;
C. Flewitt 41;
Alwyne Gardener 10,13,18;
P. Gummer x,xi,2,8,11,54,56,65,88,119,128,140;
Hammonds Photography 120,122;
C. S. Haslam 41,61,86,87;
R. Hayman
x,xi,xii,3,9,20,21,22,23,24,26,27,28,29,31,34,
35,36,37,39,41,42,43,57,61,62,66,68,69,70,71,
72,73,74,75,76,77,78,82,83,84,85,91,92,93,96,
100,101,106,107,108,110,112,113,121,123,124,
129,136,137,142,143,146,147,148,151;
D. Heath viii;
Historic Royal Palaces 48;

M. Jebb 2,130;
N. Jones 3;
M. Kent 58;
John Mills 89;
Minster Photography 79;
J. Morris
16,32,48,49,53,97,103,109,118,134,150;
Photography South West 121;
Ramsbury Photographic Services
45,47,144,145;
Reflections Photography 55,89;
D. Roberts 113;
Sonia Rolt 50,51;
Royal Commission on the
Historical Monuments of England 89;
A. Secker 29;
C. M. Smith xii,37,102,138
M. Stancliffe 30;
D. Tansey 90,149;
A. Thomas 81;
J. Tricker 149;
Turners Photography 7;
M. Watters x,50;
West Air Photography (Weston-Super-Mare)
138.

Front Cover Photograph of Woodspring Priory
by Ramsbury Photographic Services
Back Cover Photograph of Langley Gatehouse
by Archive

Maps compiled by C. S. Haslam and drawn
by European Map Graphics Ltd and Clyde
Surveys Ltd

Site maps in the Handbook are based upon
the Ordnance Survey 1:2500 maps with the
permission of the Controller of HMSO ©
Crown Copyright

Plans and site maps drawn by
Michael Fleetwood and Desmond Thomas

National Trust Cottages

The National Trust has about 180 holiday cottages in some of the most attractive areas of England, Wales and Northern Ireland. They range in style from a fairly spartan fell cottage, ideal for hikers, to a luxuriously appointed Cornish Mansion set in 11 acres of grounds. For further details telephone 0225 705676 or write to: The National Trust, PO Box 101, Western Way, Melksham, Wiltshire SN12 8EA.

Printed in Great Britain by Henry Ling Ltd., at the Dorset Press, Dorchester, Dorset